SCISSORS, NURSE, SCISSORS

The diary of a student nurse at
St Bartholomew's Hospital, London 1959-1962

Greta Barnes

IN LOVING MEMORY OF MY PARENTS
GEORGE AND EILEEN TISDALE

ACKNOWLEDGEMENTS

I would like to thank Ruth Midgley for her editorial support, encouragement and advice and Lynne Brown for her excellent design work; without these two I doubt publication of this book would ever have come to fruition.

Thanks go to St Bartholomew's Hospital Archives Department and the Department of Medical Illustrations for permission to use their images. Other photographs were taken by Priscilla Gurney's father, S. Farrant Russell. The line drawings of medical procedures and equipment are by R.N. Lane and appeared in Winifred Hector's 'Modern Nursing: theory & practice' (Heinemann). The wood engraving on page 85 depicting a Barts nurse on night duty is copyright © 1963 Simon Brett.

Thanks are also due to Sybil Allen, Mary Walker and Beth Cantrell who have been a great source of remembered information. Beth was also the artist of the skeleton and cabaret drawings. Sue King kindly provided the Barts final examination papers and Anna Barney the photograph of Matron's Ball.

OBELISK BOOKS
OF STRATFORD-UPON-AVON

First published in 2009 by Obelisk Books, Meadowside, Welcombe Hills, Stratford-upon-Avon, Warwickshire, CV37 ONR
Reprinted 2010

Printed by Salvo Design and Print Ltd.

ISBN 978-0-9557206-1-1

CONTENTS

INTRODUCTION

This book describes what it was like to train as a nurse in a London Teaching Hospital in the 1950s and 1960s. Whilst it is a personal story, it also provides a snapshot of what many British hospitals were like at the time. Discipline was often harsh but patient care was never compromised.

During my training, my father encouraged me to keep a daily hospital journal. Somewhat reluctantly I agreed. The diaries had been tucked out of sight for many years and had not been read since they were written, either by me, or anyone else. However, this year [2009], it is 50 years since I started my nursing training at St Bartholomew's Hospital in

Telephone
Kenilworth 52500

South Ways
Rounds Hill
Kenilworth
Warwickshire
27 July 1962

My dearest Greta,

I well remember writing you a letter to reach you on your first day at Bart's so I thought it would be rather nice to round it all off and send you another one to reach you on your last day there. (For the record, be it said, I have also written once or twice in between!)

3½ years! Sometimes it seems only yesterday that I saw you off at Leamington for the first (of many!) times ... sometimes it seems a deal longer.

I do so hope you have much enjoyed belonging to such a well-known

and historic community. I think you have and I don't think you have any regrets whatever on the choice you made.

I hope too that it has been an experience well worth while and one you will always be able to look back on with pleasure and affection ... and I do so hope that your happy personal affair (spelt without an 'e' at the end, note!!) of the last twelve months has not caused the 'Hospital Journal' you were keeping completely to dry up. If it has, do, somehow, in the next few weeks try to fill in the blanks. If you do this, I know, in the years to come, you will always thank me for suggesting it.

And what good friends you have made — friends Mummy and I have

London. It seemed, therefore, an appropriate time to shake the dust off the journals and to enjoy the memories, especially as my 'set' were about to celebrate our 'golden' reunion.

In readiness for the reunion, I decided to prepare an album, taking extracts from my journal and illustrating them wherever possible. Looking at the album, my friends and I reminisced and were reminded how our years at Barts had perhaps been the most formative years of our lives. This album was the starting point for 'Scissors, Nurse, Scissors', as it seemed to us that its contents would appeal to a wider readership.

For the book, I have taken sections from the diaries and illustrated them with my own photographs and others kindly lent to me by Barts Hospital. The diary entries are unsurprisingly youthful and I have left them as they were written. I have not attempted to contrast the past with the present day training for nurses. It was different then, but above all we learnt that compassion and care endured even if we were unable to cure the patient.

met and know and like to think of as our friends too. Beth, Meg, Priscilla, Anna, Mary, Jacky.....

It must, in your own words, be a very bitter-sweet day for you today, my dear. David – Barts, Barts – David. Your choice is, of course, instant, natural and overwhelmingly obvious. That it still remains bitter-sweet however indicates not one jot of doubt but rather a gracious acknowledgment to Barts for allowing you to be part of it and for accepting you within its kindly, healing walls.

.... And so, today, yet another happy era of your young life inevitably closes; but only to be the forerunner, I'm sure, of the

opening of the happiest and most fulfilling period of all. And in this, as in all other things, you have Mummy's and my fondest love.

Daddy.

This letter from my father, sent to mark the end of my nurse training in July 1962, includes a reference to my 'Hospital Journal'. It was my father who had encouraged me to start keeping a regular journal when I first began my training in May 1959.

MARCH 1958
The Interview

Walking through Smithfield Meat Market towards Barts was the first of many new experiences. The smell, the sawdust, the blood from the carcases and the cheery cockney meat porters. I went to the public conveniences which were situated nearby and was wished luck by the attendant. She knew I was there for an interview as interviews were always held on a Thursday and she said I would be accepted 'because you talk proper'.

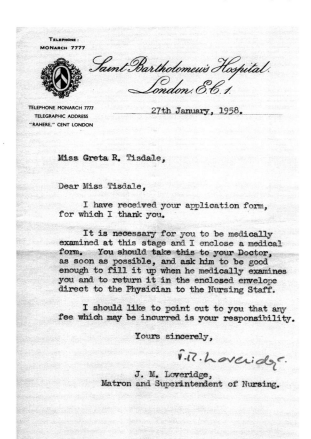

TELEPHONE:
MONARCH 7777

Saint Bartholomew's Hospital.
London. E.C.1.

TELEPHONE MONARCH 7777
TELEGRAPHIC ADDRESS
"RAHERE," CENT LONDON

27th January, 1958.

Miss Greta R. Tisdale,

Dear Miss Tisdale,

    I have received your application form, for which I thank you.

    It is necessary for you to be medically examined at this stage and I enclose a medical form. You should take this to your Doctor, as soon as possible, and ask him to be good enough to fill it up when he medically examines you and to return it in the enclosed envelope direct to the Physician to the Nursing Staff.

    I should like to point out to you that any fee which may be incurred is your responsibility.

    Yours sincerely,

    J.R. Loveridge

    J. M. Loveridge,
    Matron and Superintendent of Nursing.

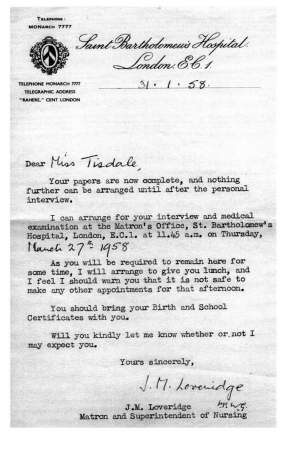

TELEPHONE:
MONARCH 7777

Saint Bartholomew's Hospital.
London. E.C.1.

TELEPHONE MONARCH 7777
TELEGRAPHIC ADDRESS
"RAHERE," CENT LONDON

31 · 1 · 58.

Dear Miss Tisdale,

    Your papers are now complete, and nothing further can be arranged until after the personal interview.

    I can arrange for your interview and medical examination at the Matron's Office, St. Bartholomew's Hospital, London, E.C.1. at 11.45 a.m. on Thursday, March 27th 1958.

    As you will be required to remain here for some time, I will arrange to give you lunch, and I feel I should warn you that it is not safe to make any other appointments for that afternoon.

    You should bring your Birth and School Certificates with you.

    Will you kindly let me know whether or not I may expect you.

    Yours sincerely,

    J. M. Loveridge

    J.M. Loveridge
    Matron and Superintendent of Nursing

Matron, Miss J.M. Loveridge, gave me my interview. She was a kindly, dignified person whose large stature reinforced her important role at Barts.

I went through Henry VIII Gateway and into the Square and joined seven other candidates in a small, stuffy room. We were all dressed in a similar fashion. My suit was brown tweed and I wore red gloves with a matching handkerchief.

The interview was daunting. Matron [Miss J.M. Loveridge] was a large woman with a kind face and looked very dignified in her black uniform dress and huge, triangular, white muslin cap. She told me that Barts only accepted one out of ten candidates who applied and she asked me searching questions and why I should be accepted. Apart from the usual 'I've always wanted to help people', I replied that I had heard that young women went to St Thomas's for their training if they were a 'lady', to Guys to have a good time and Barts if they wanted to be a good nurse. What I did not say – but what I thought – was that I liked the Barts uniform.

Saint Bartholomew's Hospital.
London. E.C.1.

TELEPHONE MONARCH 7777
TELEGRAPHIC ADDRESS
"RAHERE," CENT LONDON

1st April, 1958.

Dear Miss Tisdale,

I have much pleasure in informing you that you application for a vacancy as a Student Nurse at this Hospital has been accepted, subject to a further satisfactory medical report and Chest X-ray nearer the date of your entry.

Arrangements will be made to receive you at the Preliminary Training School on May 4th, 1959.

Uniform is provided by the Hospital. Full particulars will be sent to you nearer the date of your entry. You will be required to purchase one pair of the regulation uniform shoes on arrival at the Preliminary Training School.

May we have your vaccination and dental certificates, also a further medical certificate, about eight weeks before the date of your entry. It will be necessary for you to be successfully vaccinated before entry. The medical certificate should be a note from your Doctor stating that you are still in good health and fit to commence your training, if this is the case at that time.

I hope you will have a successful and happy training.

Will you kindly reply to me on receipt of this letter.

Yours sincerely,

J.M. Loveridge.

J. M. Loveridge.
Matron and Superintendent of Nursing.

PRELIMINARY TRAINING SCHOOL
Piggotts Manor and Aldenham Cottage

Piggotts Manor, in Letchmore Heath, was where all Barts nurses went for their preliminary training. It was a splendid manor house with glorious grounds including a lake and two tennis courts.

Aldenham Cottage with nurses playing croquet on the lawn. This is where we went to for all our meals – we loved the fresh loaves from the local baker, which we spread thickly with butter and jam.

4 MAY: Monday

Our uniforms were ready for us, all beautifully starched. Three dresses, 14 aprons, three striped belts, a navy cape lined in red, numerous collars and studs, cuffs (which would need sewing onto the dresses each time the dress was laundered) and caps. Except the caps weren't caps at all they were just a square of fine, starched, brilliant white cotton.

We were told to change into our uniform and then we would be taught how to make our caps. Will I ever learn how to do this? We were shown how they had to be folded, pinned, pleated and pinned again. Fortunately it looks as if you can wear one for a few days if you take it off carefully.

Miss Cape, the Senior Sister Tutor, directed us to a list on which there were 37 surnames, all of which were prefixed with the letter 'N'. This we were told stood for 'Nurse' and that we were never, ever, to use first names when we were on duty – ALWAYS Nurse plus the surname. First lesson learnt.

For our preliminary training we are based in Letchmore Heath, Hertfordshire, at Piggotts Manor and Aldenham Cottage (which isn't a cottage at all!). We were taken on a conducted tour of them both. They are very grand and everywhere is spotless.

I'm rooming with a really nice girl called Beth Grunsell who has arrived complete with a bell rope which she has hung over the mirror. The bedrooms are quite comfy and some, in fact, are rather palatial and have a carpet and washbasin. Ours doesn't. We have lino on the floor and a hard horsehair mattress on our beds.

We've set the alarm for 6.30 a.m. as tomorrow promises to be very full and we feel we need at least an hour in which to get up. Breakfast is at 7.50 a.m. and we have to walk to Aldenham Cottage for all our

Our 'set', the 37 who began training in May 1959, photographed with our tutors.

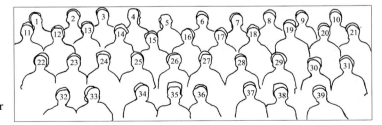

1. Barbara Miller
2. Anna Nowakowska
3. Priscilla Russell
4. Jackie Roberts
5. Ruth Johnson
6. Rosemary Waring
7. Annette Williams
8. Helen Collins
9. Elizabeth Wilson
10. Jennifer Young
11. Jane Wylie
12. Anne Whatley
13. Lorna Bastin
14. Anne Murphy
15. Pat Hines
16. Judy Knudsen
17. Frances Carpenter
18. Dorothy Linter
19. Emma Thompson
20. Beth Grunsell
21. Margaret Robbins
22. Susan Sykes
23. Anne Houldershaw
24. Terry Workman
25. Mary Gunn
26. Miss Miles
27. Miss Cape
28. Carol Harvey
29. Sally Murray
30. Margaret Reid
31. Angela Gaddum
32. Judith Edwards
33. Gayle Palmer
34. Linda Carmichael
35. Greta Tisdale
36. Jackie Randall
37. Sallie Phelps
38. Paula Farmer
39. Joan Addison

My laundry mark, the number 712 will never be forgotten. All the marks had to be neatly sewn on to all garments. I was so slow that Beth had to help me finish the task.

A hospital corner. For years I had wanted to know how to achieve this procedure and now, thanks to the clear demonstrations by the Sister Tutors, I did.

meals. The house is about five minutes' walk away, through a beautiful orchard full of apple blossom.

5 MAY: Tuesday

Today has been very full. We haven't had a minute since we got up. I was a little quicker than yesterday at struggling into my uniform. The caps are clearly going to be a problem. We are not allowed to wear any make up, earrings or other jewellery and our hair has to be pushed behind our ears.

We saw round the house and learnt about our household duties. Then it was to the classroom for anatomy and the theory of bandaging and then the practical. We learnt how to make a hospital bed. How will we possibly be able to make one in three minutes even if we do work in pairs? We are told mitring a corner of a sheet ensures that the bottom sheet remains taut and that when we are making beds it is an opportunity to talk to patients when they are well enough and if they are too ill it requires the nurse's undivided attention, in other words it is not an opportunity to talk to the other nurse.

This afternoon we had to sew laundry marks onto our uniform. All 40 of them – what a bind. Now I have sewn them on I am absolutely determined to stick the next three years. We also had to embroider our name on the red inside of our cape, mine looks very poor. I'm no seamstress. We were fitted for our uniform shoes by a representative from Daniel Neal the outfitters. Seventy shillings [£3.50] a pair and we have to buy two pairs.

Off duty – see I'm already getting into the jargon – at 5 p.m. We

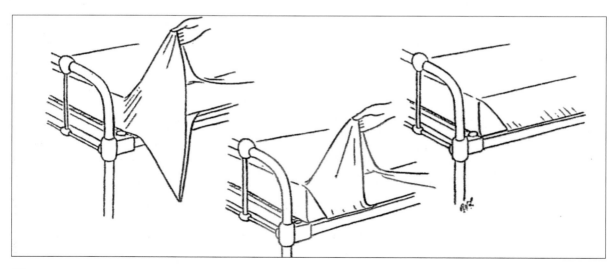

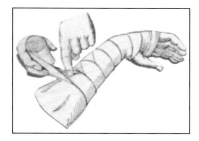

Figure of 8 bandages in use on an arm and a leg. We also had to learn how to recognise and use many other types, including capellines used for the head and many-tailed bandages for the abdomen.

played tennis for half an hour before supper. The grounds really are superb and apart from two tennis courts there is a lake and beautiful gardens. After this we went to find the two shops in Letchmore Heath. These both catered for everything 'the nurses wanted' including white kirby grips to keep our hair back and a small library of about 40 books, 30 of which had the word 'Doctor' or 'Nurse' in the title.

6 MAY: Wednesday

We rose at about 7 a.m., a sure sign that we'll get later as time goes by. Another heavenly day. I feel as though I have known everyone for years – we are having a whale of a time.

Started housework with a vengeance. I'm cleaning the classroom and conservatory – the sisters are very particular – there is apparently a correct way of doing everything, whether it is damp dusting, dry dusting or simply sweeping a floor. We have been told always to stand back and to be critical of our endeavours but also to take pleasure with the results, however menial the task. A job well done.

Prof. Garrod arrived at Piggotts Manor this afternoon to carry out Schick tests [to check susceptibility to diphtheria] on all of us. My goodness, Miss Cape was 'Sirring' him all over the place. 'Yes, Sir.' 'No, Sir.' 'Three bags full, Sir'.

A practical bandaging class next. Will I ever get these spirals, figure of 8's, 'T' bandages, many-tailed and capellines sorted out?

8 MAY: Friday

I am so embarrassed. Paul R. has sent me some carnations. I could have died – however, everyone was very envious.

It is amazing how many of the girls' fathers are Barts trained doctors. Apart from doctors' daughters, there are several vicars' daughters and Beth's father is a professor of veterinary medicine.

11 MAY: Monday

Oh, what a lot there is to learn – but it is all such fun.

We had practical cookery this afternoon and had to cut paper-thin bread and butter. I was not very successful. Then we had to practise carrying a tray on one arm. Apparently, when we are on the wards we ALWAYS have to carry everything, from a glass of water to a full meal, on a tray even if this means that we have to retrace our steps up the ward to replace the tray.

I had my pyjamas and blouse confiscated from the laundry this morning – was I livid! I had just ironed them and there they were, all screwed up in a ball in the office. Apparently I should have moved them before breakfast.

15 MAY: Friday

I had six letters this morning including one from Ian B. asking me to a Commem. Ball at Oxford in June. I don't think I dare ask for time off. I was summoned to see Miss Cape this evening because Walter M. had managed to get the telephone number of the PTS [Preliminary Training School] office. Miss Cape was fairly understanding but said it must not happen again. I phoned Walter and told him I thought it wasn't advisable to go out with a male acquaintance while I'm here.

25 MAY: Monday

I heard this morning that I will be spending my first three months as a 'pro.' [probationer] on a male surgical ward at Barts. This afternoon we went up to the hospital and I spent a couple of hours on the ward I will be on, which is called Fleet Street.

Nursing real live patients at last! It was such a thrill to hear a patient's grateful 'Thank you Nurse,' just for a plain cup of tea.

Poor Meg Robbins is starting at Hill End Hospital, a branch of Barts, in St. Albans, which is where she lives, so she is very upset. She, and the others who went to Hill End, were disappointed as the hospital was run down and untidy, unlike Barts which was spotless.

29 MAY: Friday

Pay day today! Our Training Allowance is £273 for our first year increasing to £299 in our third, subject to deductions for Health and National Insurance and Superannuation Contributions. £123 are going to be deducted each year for Board and Lodging. We are paid monthly but if you work out the amount per week it is £2 17s 6d [£2.87], out of which we have to buy all our toiletries and black stockings. To think some of the girls here who did a job before starting their training were earning £11 with everything deducted. We do get all our food included and the meals here are excellent, especially the fresh bread and jam we have for tea when we are all ravenous.

Carol Harvey and Jackie Randall have each bought a motor scooter. Poor Carol, no sooner had she arrived back here with her newly acquired Lambretta when she ran into the hedge and got a dent in the front mudguard!

8 JUNE: Monday

To Barts again for another visit. Oh it was wonderful! I had to bed bath a patient – yes I did remember the creases Miss Cape. He had had a gastrectomy and had tubes leading in all directions. After this I 'did teas', then made hordes of beds, 'did a back' and measured some urine. Then I was told by Miss Davies, one of our sister tutors, to report to the

My weekly pay. This photograph shows the grand sum of £2 17s 6d, which had to cover essentials such as toiletries and black stockings, as well as all our clothes and travel costs.

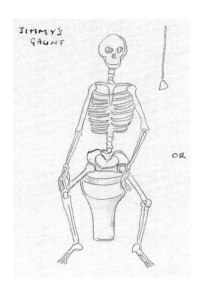

Jimmy, one of our skeletons, drawn in an unusual situation by Beth Grunsell. If anyone had been caught using the skeleton for purposes of amusement, we would have all been in serious trouble.

Nurse's scissors. These were an essential tool used for cutting a multitude of items. Every nurse carried her own pair in the top pocket of her uniform.

ward sister. I did this and was told in no uncertain terms to 'Go away, I'm much too busy to see you'. So I did, without a murmur. What an injustice. But we are not allowed to speak up for ourselves.

I nearly forgot to mention, I served tea to Sir George – or was his name William? He asked me to ask someone to get him a blanket and I completely forgot. Poor soul, he must have frozen. It's interesting that there was a 'Sir' on the ward. He was in a side room and seemed like a private patient – but Barts does not have private patients.

24 JUNE: Wednesday
Last night one of our skeletons, I'm not sure whether it was Jimmy or Fred, was taken from the practical room and was seated on the lavatory. Imagine the surprise of one unsuspecting nurse as she walked in, in the half light. The poor girl nearly had a heart attack!

29 JUNE: Monday
My third visit to Barts. I hardly know where to start. The first alarm went off at 6 a.m. which was set just to prepare us for the 6.45 a.m. one. What an effort to get up. Beth and I plunged into the bath 'toutes les deux'. 7 a.m. saw us frantically getting dressed and then off to do the housework before breakfast. Full speed ahead with the duster and then over to Aldenham Cottage for bacon, tomato, toast and marmalade and a cup of tea to swill it all down.

We all got the usual jitters on the way up to Barts – however mine soon went once I got onto the ward.

My first job was to make up an operation bed, then carbolise two more. After this another pro. and I made up five beds for the new admissions before we served the patients their morning drinks. I also did some backs, measured urine and tidied the kitchen and sluice.

Then disaster struck. I was walking down the ward and suddenly a houseman came from behind the curtained bed with his hands dripping with blood.

'Scissors, Nurse, Scissors.'

'Scissors? Scissors?' I couldn't even think what scissors were. As luck would have it I instinctively went to my top pocket and produced my scissors. So far, so good. Then he asked me to cut some plaster for him. Where should I cut it? Near the barrel? In the middle? At the end? We are taught exactly how to do procedures in the classroom so I felt sure there must be a correct place. Anyway, I compromised by cutting it between the barrel and the middle. He didn't complain.

Next, laying up for lunch. Every patient has a polished wooden locker and a crisp cotton cloth on which the cutlery is laid.

Sister served out the food at 12 noon sharp, carefully wiping round

Fahrenheit thermometer.
No centigrade or digital thermometers for us! We soon became skilled at checking the level of the mercury column against the scale in Farenheit marked on the glass. A person's 'normal' temperature was 98.4°F.

Meg's Birthday Cabaret.
Several of us wore make-shift fancy dress and performed our various party pieces. Beth captured the hilarity of the evening in her usual artistic manner.

the edge of each plate for any spills. Meanwhile all the nurses stood in a queue and took it in turns to take the food – on a tray, of course – to the patients. All the patients who needed feeding were fed by nurses sitting at their bedside.

Our lunchtime next, for which we get half an hour. One of the nurses told me that if we go off late for lunch we still have to be back on duty within the allocated half an hour.

I was so hungry by this time and the food here is so good. Soup, lamb and potatoes or steak and kidney pie or salad, then sago or gooseberries and custard, cheese and biscuits and finally a cup of tea. Chatter, we never stopped.

After lunch we all met our sister tutors to have a tour round an operating theatre and sterilising room. Clean? There wasn't a speck of dirt anywhere.

Back to the ward at 2 p.m. More drinks to be served. More tidying up to do and then some 'TPRs' [temperature, pulse and respiration rates] to take before teatime. One patient had a respiratory rate of 32, a rise from 20 in the morning. When I said this to another pro., who was just one set above us, she said, 'I should just put down 20 like it was this morning' – but when she saw his temperature had also risen, she checked the respirations and agreed it was 32, so I had to report the matter to the staff nurse.

In one of the side wards was the Provost of Southwark Cathedral whose wife is also 'warded' [an inpatient] in Barts. She was visiting him for tea and told me that both of her children had got measles – it sounds as if the family are in a pretty poor way at the moment all things considered.

Gayle Palmer got it in the neck and is in trouble with the nurses on her ward. Apparently when she went back to PTS after our last visit she had asked Miss Cape whether it was necessary to have a cover on an inhaler as there hadn't been one on the inhaler she was told to give to a patient. Miss Cape just said, 'Oh, didn't they have a cover? Well they should have done.' Anyway after this she wrote a stinking letter to the ward sister, who was furious with the nurses who swore black and blue that they had used a cover. Poor Gayle. It was only meant to be a casual comment. Everything is very strict here. We arrived back at Piggotts exhausted but happy.

3 JULY: Friday
Cabaret night to celebrate Meg's birthday. Ten of us thought we would have a party. We were stopped in our tracks when we were mid cabaret in Barbara Miller's room. (Barbara has her own room because she is 23.) Barbara was already in bed dressed in a black nightdress with pins

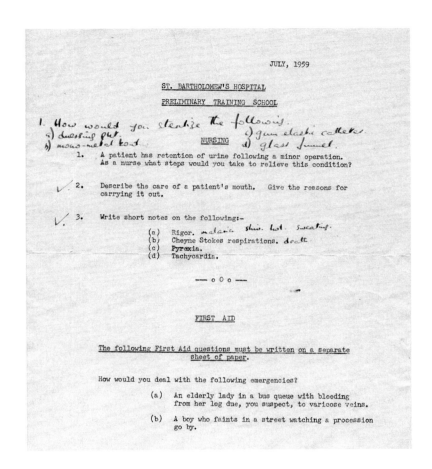

JULY, 1959

ST. BARTHOLOMEW'S HOSPITAL

PRELIMINARY TRAINING SCHOOL

1. How would you sterilize the following.
a) dressing put   e) gum elastic catheter
b) mono-metal tool   NURSING   d) glass funnel

1. A patient has retention of urine following a minor operation. As a nurse what steps would you take to relieve this condition?

✓ 2. Describe the care of a patient's mouth. Give the reasons for carrying it out.

✓ 3. Write short notes on the following:-
   (a) Rigor. malaria shiv. hot. sweating.
   (b) Cheyne Stokes respirations. death.
   (c) Pyrexia.
   (d) Tachycardia.

— o O o —

FIRST AID

The following First Aid questions must be written on a separate sheet of paper.

How would you deal with the following emergencies?

   (a) An elderly lady in a bus queue with bleeding from her leg due, you suspect, to varicose veins.

   (b) A boy who faints in a street watching a procession go by.

The PTS Nursing examination paper. We had a nasty moment when we found it included a question on the retention of urine, which we hadn't learnt about.

in her hair and white stuff on her face and in walked Miss Davies. Well what could we do? Luckily she roared with laughter but she did pack us off to bed. Interestingly, Miss Davies trained at St Thomas's Hospital and apparently is one of only a very few trained nurses at Barts who isn't Barts trained.

7 JULY: Tuesday
The dreaded PTS exams. The first question on the Nursing paper was on the retention of urine which was a topic we hadn't covered. PANIC! Fortunately Miss Cape realised and she was able to contact the Nursing School and get it altered to sterilisation.
   I just hope our dreaded Saturday tests have helped.

10 JULY: Friday
The amazing weather has broken – after ten weeks of almost unbroken sunshine.
   We literally turned the house upside down today. I turned out what seemed like hundreds of cupboards and scrubbed all the shelves. No wonder the place was so spotless when we arrived. A lesson I suppose which we are being taught. Leave the place as you would like to find it.
   Anne Houldershaw is giving us a lesson on how to hitchhike. She often manages to hitch her whole way home. I'm not planning to tell my parents or they might get worried.

11 JULY: Saturday
We had a wonderful time this afternoon. Eight of us were invited to a Garden Party which was being given for the disabled servicemen from the Star and Garter Home, Richmond and had been organised by the RAF. A lot of the men were from the First World War. We just had to look pretty, talk to them, wheel their wheelchairs and generally help

Some of our set, photographed during our PTS days. The photo includes Greta, Beth, Meg and Prissy, who would go on to become life-long friends.

Queen Mary's Nurses' Home, where we went from PTS ready to start work on the wards. It was an imposing building inside the hospital precincts. Communal facilities included the Isla Stewart Library, a large sitting room and nurses' hairdressing salon. We each had our own bedroom – but they were tiny.

them. Some of the men never have any visitors and were so grateful for anything we did for them. I spent my time with a poor old chap who used to be a blacksmith's apprentice. He was so lonely and couldn't speak properly. There were tears when we said goodbye.

13 JULY: Monday
We passed! At least all of us did except Annette, which overshadowed our joy. However, we cheered up this evening and had a hilarious party and sing-song and toasted each other in lemonade.

21 JULY: Tuesday
Back to the grind. We are all feeling nervous about going on the wards tomorrow and are giving each other moral support.

We have moved into Queen Mary's Nurses' Home just off the Square. It is huge and seems to be full of corridors. We were shown two lovely sitting rooms and the Isla Stewart Library and also the nurses' hairdressing salon.

We are all on the sixth floor. I have been trying to sort out my bedroom. It is about the size of a matchbox, really, it is tiny. What floor there is, is covered in brown lino and it's a long way along the corridor to the bathroom.

There are two lovely black maids on our floor. One of them is called Maud and the other Amelia. We are told that they will be cleaning our rooms, making our beds and bringing us breakfast in bed twice a month. What a treat.

Apparently we are allowed two late passes a week until 12 midnight, which have to be signed by the ward sister, otherwise we have to be in by 10.30 p.m. In exceptional cases we can obtain an extended late pass from Matron until 2.30 a.m.

As we are new probationers we have to sit at the lowliest position in the Nurses' Dining Room. Nobody, however, had told us this before we had our first meal – but we were soon put right. We had mixed grill for supper including kidneys – fancy, for our first meal, they were not content just to put kidneys on our exam paper!

We have been told that if we are wearing our cloaks and stop to speak to a sister, even if we are out in the Square in midwinter, we must remove them. Also that we must never have a ladder in our stockings.

MEN'S SURGICAL
Fleet Street Ward

St Bartholomew the Less, the hospital church. Barts is unique in being the only English hospital that is a parish in its own right. **Sisters going to prayer.** For many, religion played a major role in their nursing vocation.

22 JULY: Wednesday

At last the years of waiting are over. I'm really at Barts and a real pro.

We were woken at 6.20 a.m. by the clanging of a hand-held bell which was being rung up and down all the corridors. This apparently happens every morning regardless as to whether the sleeping nurses are on duty or not.

Beth and I went to Communion at 7 a.m. at St Bartholomew the Less, for some spiritual refreshment. There were quite a number of sisters in the congregation. We are told that Barts is unique among hospitals in being a parish in its own right. The little church is certainly special.

On duty at 1.30 p.m. until 8 p.m. My feet are killing me but it was as good as I had hoped. I only hope that I shall be as enthusiastic this time next week.

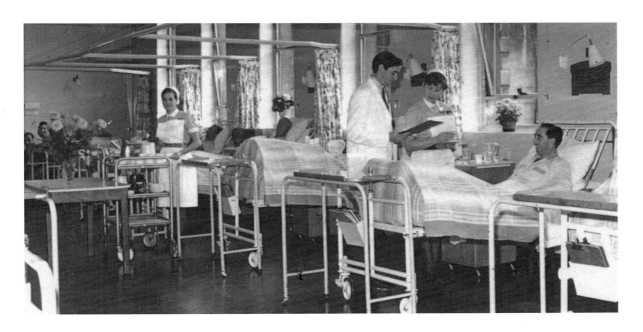

Male surgical wards were always busy and the East End cockneys so often a source of delight. In hospital jargon, medical students on surgical wards were called 'dressers', whereas those on medical wards were known as 'clerks'.

24 JULY: Friday

I'm dead! I worked from 7.30 a.m. until 8.20 p.m. (with 10 a.m. until 1.30 p.m. off, when I went back to bed). It's not really that the hours are so very long but that they feel as though they are because we start early and finish late.

I carried out mouth care for a very sick patient, gave out numerous bedpans and bottles and post-operative Friars Balsam inhalers. I rubbed backs and bottoms, cleaned lockers, carbolised three beds and mattresses, made 'hundreds' of beds, (wheels turned in, openings of pillow cases facing away from the door), buttered bread, served tea and transported meals (always on a tray) that had been served out beautifully by sister.

One of the second year nurses told me she was 'just going through'. 'Through where?', I said. Another lesson learnt. 'Going through' is another way of saying going to the lavatory.

25 JULY: Saturday

A lovely day. I am beginning to feel less of a spare part. One of my jobs today was to ask all the patients if they had had 'one for the book', i.e., had they 'had their bowels open'. We are having to learn all these Barts terms. Another job was to vacuum the ward, as well as clean and polish the lockers because it is the weekend, when Milly, the domestic dragon,

19

doesn't work. Milly frightens me to death. She thinks she is second in command (and she is) and keeps saying she will report us to sister on the ward.

I was washing Dr de Savitsch today and noticed he had a book by his bed which I had read, called 'In Search of Complications', and then I realised he had written it and that he is a famous American surgeon who was originally from Russia. What a thrill.

Tonight several of us sat on the stairs in the Nurses' Home looking into one of the operating theatres where an operation on an enormous woman was in progress. Suddenly the operating table collapsed. Fortunately the woman was caught before she hit the ground – it was just as well she was unconscious!

2 AUGUST: Sunday

Meg came up from Hill End this evening. To my astonishment Prissy [Priscilla Russell] climbed along the window ledge – remember we are six floors up – and into Barbara's room and opened the door so Meg has got a bed for the night. (Barbara is warded as she is anaemic.)

Prissy was not daunted by heights and seized her chance to walk along a window ledge six floors up! Her father had completed his medical training at Barts before becoming a medical missionary.

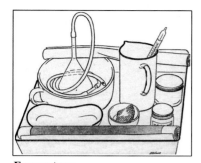

Enema tray

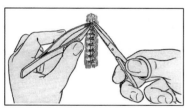

Removing stitches

3 AUGUST: Monday

I have given an enema – the first of many I suspect. I wonder how soon familiarity will breed contempt. I have also taken stitches out for the first time – what a thrill. The patient was very long-suffering and said it didn't hurt at all – I wonder?

The Mobile Trolley Service visited the ward this afternoon. Apparently it comes on a Monday and Friday and the patients can buy toilet requisites, writing paper, sweets and postage stamps, etc. It's a voluntary service and I gather it is run by the consultants' wives. There is also a lending library where the librarians visit each ward every week with a book trolley and a bedside telephone service. I think the patients at Barts are very well catered for.

The weather has been absolutely gorgeous today and some of the long stay patients have been wheeled into the Square in their beds to enjoy the sunshine.

8 AUGUST: Saturday

The weather is very close today. Apart from Dr de Savitsch the patients seem to be progressing rapidly. He said to me this morning, 'I had no idea it would be so hard to die, why can't it be done with quickly?'

Beth and I went into Barts the Less this evening – we found it so peaceful and helpful.

The mobile bedside trolley service provided by Barts was greatly appreciated by patients on the wards. This useful service was run on a voluntary basis by the wives of the Barts consultants.

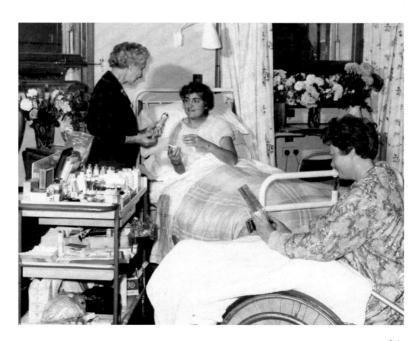

Fleet Street and Harmsworth firm. This was made up of consultants, registrars, sisters and other medical staff working on these two surgical wards, which were situated in close proximity on either side of a corridor

25 AUGUST: Tuesday
Sister Fleet Street seems to think I am too extravagant with the tea and sugar and has told me to be more economical when I am doing the trolley and making the teas and coffees.

I was left in charge of the ward for half an hour today. It was just as well it wasn't an operations or 'On Duty' day (when emergencies are admitted). I felt very proud and very scared.

Yet another lovely day, apparently we have had the best summer for 80 years. London is very hot and I do miss the country.

13 SEPTEMBER: Sunday
I gave my first injection today on Mr Passingham in the 'upper outer quadrant of the right buttock'. He seemed quite happy but I felt most peculiar.

David P., the houseman on Fleet Street, has asked me out to coffee three times now and I can't make up my mind whether to go or not.

24 SEPTEMBER: Thursday
Several of us tried to get into the Podola Trial at the Old Bailey this morning during our split duty. One of the perks of being in uniform is that we are allowed access through the front door without having to queue with everyone else. Unfortunately we were just too late to get in. [The trial lasted two days and Gunther Podola became the last man to be executed in Britain for killing a policeman.]

28 SEPTEMBER: Monday
Our set's Election Day. This is when matron, the sister tutors and the ward sisters decide whether we have reached a high enough standard and are suitable to continue our training. I passed, as did all my close friends but sadly five failed – Jackie, Emma, Elizabeth, Pat and Rosemary. They have one more chance and if they fail again they will have to leave.

Those of us who passed are now allowed to carry a basket, of our own choice, and to wear a Barts scarf. Apart from that nothing has changed.

I have to go to sickrooms tomorrow to see Dr Coulson because I have lost several pounds in weight. What do they expect, the way we have to charge around?

30 SEPTEMBER: Wednesday

I felt rather depressed this morning – my first death. I was holding Percy Smith's hand while the houseman was putting in a drip when Mr Smith suddenly had a fit and died quite suddenly. His poor wife – he was all she had. Last night she told me that they meant everything to each other as they had no children. She was such a darling.

When I went to see Dr Coulson yesterday he 'prescribed' bars of chocolate to help me gain weight. Fantastic!

The list for changing wards has just gone up. I shall be going to Annie Zunz Ward which is a women's medical ward. I shall be so sorry to leave Fleet Street.

Proud probationers carrying their baskets out of the Square. The right to carry a basket was granted only to those who were successful on 'Election Day'.

My basket. Choosing a basket was an important task as this was one way of showing our individuality when wearing uniform.

WOMEN'S MEDICAL
Annie Zunz Ward

DAYS

4 OCTOBER: Sunday
Annie Zunz was fun today but Sister comes back tomorrow and I am dreading it because I believe she is awful. I really mustn't let myself get too disheartened. The patients are lovely and the ward very busy. We didn't finish until 8.30 p.m. and if it wasn't one patient being incontinent it was another.

14 OCTOBER: Wednesday
Sister really isn't too bad as long as you keep on the right side of her. She is young, dark and attractive but is quite moody and unpredictable. I heard her swearing today, back to a patient who was swearing at her, which was interesting as we have just heard that she is leaving Barts shortly to become a medical missionary!

  I am really enjoying nursing women but they are quite exhausting compared with men. I think they require more mental effort, but they really appreciate all we do for them and unlike the men they like to be neat and tidy and they don't spit all the time. I am not fond of sputum.

17 OCTOBER: Saturday
When Sister asked Mrs Piggott, aged 87, what religion she belonged to she replied, 'Oh just ordinary my dear, just ordinary'. She is a delight – little and cuddly but in so much pain.

25 OCTOBER: Sunday
I cannot believe this. Yesterday I went from ward to ward to try and track down a cup and saucer and plate which we had lost. This morning Sister summoned me to her room, and gave me a dressing down because she said that three separate sisters, all independent of each other, had reported to her that one of her nurses (me) in search of lost crockery had come on their ward saying she was from Annie. I just didn't think to say Annie Zunz. Honestly, you would think that sisters with patients dying on their hands would have better things to notice.

7 NOVEMBER: Saturday
Friends John O. and Simon H. came down today from Cambridge. Beth is in sickrooms so couldn't join us but even so we had a good time and

---

Day Duty Hours

Duty Span: 7.30 a.m. to 8 p.m.
 - Four days a week, 3 hours off duty.
 - Two evenings a week, 4 hours off duty.
 - One day a week, a whole day off duty, with an evening off beforehand.
With the subtraction of meal times, this is a 49-hour week on the wards.

A sickroom, where nurses were able to recuperate in pleasant and quiet surroundings away from the hubbub of the wards.

Helen, the Post Keeper, was a great favourite in the hospital. She knew the name of every nurse.
The 'fifth' nurse, who sterilised the instruments, also had the enviable job of collecting the post.

went out for a gorgeous meal at Albert's, Beak Street. We went there by taxi too. After the meal we went on to a wonderful concert at the Royal Festival Hall.

Coming back, as we got to the Smithfield Gate, the clock struck midnight and the porter was closing the gate. Do you think he would let the boys in? This place gets more and more like a convent.

8 NOVEMBER: Sunday
Miss Ormeston (Ormy), who is the motherly Sickrooms Sister, invited the boys and me to visit Beth and to have tea. She obviously smelt romance in the air, and she loves a bit of romance, so she removed everyone else out of the sitting room and gave us a cosy tea party with the crusts cut off the delicate sandwiches. She is such a joy.

Miss Dye, the Home Sister, walked in on our party unsuspectingly and you should have seen her face, it was a picture.

Not surprisingly Beth is feeling much better!

11 NOVEMBER: Wednesday
I did 'fifth nursing' this morning which was great fun. It meant I was in charge of the sterilising room and then, the best bit, I walked round the hospital with the butcher's basket delivering and picking up items. I felt very grand. The most important task was collecting the post for everyone on the ward. Helen, the Post Keeper, is one of the most popular people in the hospital and seems to know everybody and their name. Receiving post is so important to us all and we keep unopened letters tucked under the bibs of our aprons in readiness to read later.

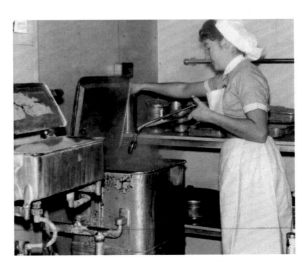

NIGHTS

14 NOVEMBER: Saturday

My first night is over. The 'night stripe' [third year], Corrinne Everson, and I were on duty from 7.50 p.m. until 8.15 a.m. without a break. There is no 'twilight nurse' [fourth year] on a Saturday hence we have to stay all night on the ward. Twilight nurses work from 4 p.m. until just after midnight on weekdays.

After the Report we said prayers and settled the patients. I went into the kitchen to wash up the cups and saucers and was greeted enthusiastically with wild gesticulations and stocking waving and blinds whizzing up and down from the Nurses' Home. It was, of course, Beth, Anna Nowakowska and Mary Gunn, etc., who haven't yet started night duty.

After washing up, the cleaning started with a vengeance. I scrubbed, sterilised and polished what felt like hundreds of bedpans and then gave the sluice its nightly spring clean.

Supper was brought up to the ward and we took turns to have it in the kitchen. Then it was sanitary towel time. Sanitary towels are known as Martha pads at Barts and monthly periods as 'having Martha'. The Martha pads have to be rolled and packed into drums ready for sterilisation. Apart from taking patients bedpans and making comforting cups of tea, the early hours were spent virtually in the dark, standing at a table in the middle of the ward and packing, packing, packing. If it wasn't Martha pads it was dressings. By 3 a.m. I thought the night would never end.

Good news and a surprise. Corrinne made me tea (this a tradition where the senior nurse cooks for the pro.). She cooked me scrambled eggs on toast which were delicious. She told me to expect some form of egg every night as that is all there is in the ward kitchen.

We managed to make all 27 beds before the day nurses and sister arrived and after the Night Report we were finally off duty.

How, how, how am I going to manage three months of this? The thought of having to work 10 nights without a break is daunting.

Bedpans were the most important items of a pro's life on the ward: either giving them to a patient or washing and polishing them until they gleamed!

A bedroom in the Night Nurses' Home in Bryanston Square. We were taken each night by bus to Barts to go on duty and then back the next morning.

I have moved into the Night Nurses' Home in Bryanston Square, Marylebone, which is meant to be quiet in the daytime while we are sleeping. I have bought two Spencers to wear under my uniform, and two pairs of warm pyjamas and a hot water bottle in the hope I will be lulled to sleep in the day.

15 NOVEMBER: Sunday
I did not sleep a wink all day.
   Tonight was very hectic. Lizzie Reynolds was admitted. Apparently Lizzie had been a circus trapeze artist when she had had a terrible fall and broken her neck. She is quadraplegic and has pneumonia and cannot cough anything up. She has now had a tracheotomy and requires very careful nursing. What a wonderful woman – even though she cannot talk she is always smiling.
   I'm exhausted.

19 NOVEMBER: Thursday
It was Gayle's first night last night and apparently she felt tired in the middle of the night so off she popped into an empty side room for forty winks. The night sister had done her round so she thought she was safe. But no, the night sister had smelt a rat and came back to the ward. Gayle was in big trouble.

24 NOVEMBER: Tuesday
At last, four nights off. Home for some wonderful rest!

28 NOVEMBER: Saturday
The patients made it worth coming back. Poor Mrs Cowley died in the night. We can only be relieved. She was in such pain and we could do nothing. She kept crying out and we both felt so helpless. Corrinne and I laid her out – for me it was the first time – and at last she looked so peaceful. I was meant to be at Martin W.'s 21st birthday celebration last night and it was so far removed, looking after a dying woman.

1 DECEMBER: Tuesday
I only had half an hour's sleep yesterday. I just cannot sleep in the day. The only time I get a proper sleep is when I have a late call. We have a couple of these during our ten-night stint, when we don't go on duty until 11.15 p.m. Inevitably on these occasions I get to sleep at about 4 p.m., when it's getting dark, and then I am in a deep sleep when I'm woken up at 10 p.m. to catch the bus to Barts.
   Poor Mrs Piggott and Mrs Belch are dying. Mrs Piggott asked me to write some items down that she wants to leave to her nephew. She

27

wants to die now and says, 'I just want to go to sleep and not to wake up again'.

2 DECEMBER: Wednesday
Both Mrs Piggott and Mrs Belch died during the night. I know it is for the best for both of them but I still can't help feeling miserable. All Sister could do this morning when she came on duty was complain. Maybe she was upset too, but I was told off for two things I hadn't even done – I could have wept.

15 DECEMBER: Tuesday
My birthday. I have had lots of cards and presents and my parents sent me a gorgeous birthday cake from Fortnum and Mason. However for the first time since I started at Barts I feel homesick.

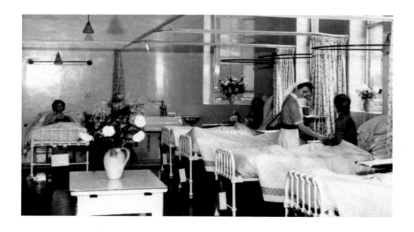

We had to tidy the ward as often as four times a day, especially before a consultant did his round. We even had to make sure the wheels of the beds were always turned inwards at the same angle.

26 DECEMBER: Saturday
Back to the grind after nights off and a lovely Christmas at home. I missed the train and John O. drove me back but we didn't arrive until 5 p.m. and we have to be in by 4 p.m. Beth arrived at the same moment and we crept in together holding hands. To our surprise the warden was lenient and we wished we had stayed out another couple of hours. Anyway, we didn't go to bed – we just sat and played 'La Mer' over and over and over again. Yet another death. Poor Maudie Clark. She had a horrible death and one that I will never forget. Thank goodness none of her relations was there.

29 DECEMBER: Tuesday
Great excitement here tonight. The Nurses' Home is being guarded and there are police everywhere. Apparently there is a manic murderer in the vicinity. Golly, we were very scared and I hardly dared go into the sluice alone.

30 DECEMBER: Wednesday
Miss Russell, the Night Superintendent, whom we call Jane after the film star Jane Russell, really is the limit. She is tiny and owl-like and looks as if she has never seen the light of day – but she is an ogre! She

came into the ward tonight and I was told off for removing the screens in front of the ward door too early when a patient who had died from Dalziel, the ward opposite, was being taken to the mortuary. Corrinne was in trouble because she hadn't had time to report a minor incident and we were told we would probably be sent to Matron.

I took prayers for the first time this evening. The same prayer is said on all wards:

> *'Lighten our darkness we beseech thee. O Lord;*
> *and by thy great mercy defend us from all perils and*
> *dangers of this night; for the love of thy only Son, our*
> *Saviour Jesus Christ. Amen.'*

However we are allowed to add our own prayers if we wish. The patients always say how much it means to them. It doesn't seem to matter to which faith they belong.

31 DECEMBER: Thursday
Well, my welcome to the New Year was certainly different from any I have had before. Lizzie Reynolds turned blue and as we were sucking her out we suddenly heard the bells of St Paul's Cathedral ringing in the New Year. Although Lizzie can't talk she just smiled at us and I whispered 'Happy New Year' in her ear. I wouldn't swop this for a party.

Ten minutes after midnight the houseman walked in armed with a bottle of whisky and absolutely sozzled. It was just as well we had managed to sort Lizzie out before he arrived.

1 JANUARY: Friday
Miss Doree (with cor pulmonale), who is usually miserable, has been a changed person over the last few days. She has been cheerful and sweet and I wondered why. She said to me last night that seeing Lizzie smiling so sweetly and patiently had made her feel an utter wretch. What an inspiration Lizzie has been to us all. Even though she knows she can never get better, she has helped so many people on the road to recovery.

2 JANUARY: Saturday
Gayle is leaving. She sent in her resignation yesterday. I'm sorry she is going because she is a great character and a lot of fun. She is older than most of us and has found it hard. She looks tired and fed up.

9 JANUARY: Saturday
Not content with the misery of coming back after nights off, we have just heard that our holidays have been changed. We are so upset and

furious. They are now in June, so we will have worked over a year without a holiday.

Excitement! Gayle did a moonlight flit after Matron's Ball at the Grosvenor House Hotel. She just didn't arrive back on night duty at 2.30 a.m. So she has gone with no 'goodbyes'.

Lizzie has had her tracheotomy tube removed today so let's keep our fingers crossed.

12 JANUARY: Tuesday

What a night! Lizzie stopped breathing. Oh it was dreadful. I dashed to get the sucker and phoned for Night Sister while Nurse Henderson clamped on the oxygen. She then tried to suck her out while I applied artificial respiration – by this time Lizzie was unconscious, deathly white and looked as if she had died. Her pulse and blood pressure were not recordable. Fortunately, Night Sister arrived and then two housemen appeared. They laryingoscoped her and gave her intravenous aminophylline and then she was put flat with blocks at the end of the bed so her head was lower than her body. At last all was well. Thank goodness she can't remember much. She was so near death. Somehow we just couldn't let her die.

15 JANUARY: Friday

Lizzie is no better. She looks so pale and old now but is fully conscious. She has had her 'tracky' [tracheotomy tube] put back. I wonder if she will still be with us when I get on tonight?

16 JANUARY: Saturday

Lizzie is definitely improving. Isn't it marvellous?

I'm feeling so down this morning. Jane [Miss Russell] pounced on me at about 7 a.m. She had looked at the long list of 'washings' and she wanted to know how many I had done. I had left out two as Corrinne and I thought they were quite capable of washing themselves. She was not amused – but honestly we have 27 patients, including two patients almost in diabetic comas and Lizzie, and only the two of us to cope. I feel so guilty. Why are we all so sensitive? Goodness knows what Sister Annie Zunz will say. I shall go straight down in her estimation. Will I ever 'stripe'?

17 JANUARY: Sunday

I am beginning to realise that Jane puts the fear of God in us but never actually reports us to anyone. What a relief.

We can go on holiday after all. Thank goodness as four of us had paid a deposit on a skiing trip which is going to cost us £28.

18 JANUARY: Monday
Miss Brewer, the Deputy Night Superintendent, remarked how tidy and clean our outhouses (sluice, bathrooms, sterilising room, kitchen) were. Why isn't there more praise like that? It gives one much more incentive to work.

24 JANUARY: Sunday
I have to give the Night Report to Jane tomorrow night. She frightens the living daylights out of me.

25 JANUARY: Monday
Butter wouldn't melt in her mouth! She was in such a benevolent mood, it felt too good to be true. She was absolutely sweet. She congratulated me on the report and even remarked on how good it was to Corrinne.

Poor Emma, Elizabeth, Jackie and Rosemary failed their Elections again. So that's that. Isn't it terrible? The poor souls have already said their 'goodbyes'. Golly, we are already down to 30 in our set.

St Paul's at night. The majestic cathedral seems even grander by night while the city sleeps. It was special for us to work so near to this major London landmark.

27 JANUARY: Wednesday
Several of us went for a walk round Smithfield Meat Market between 12 midnight and 12.30 a.m. It was most amusing and so busy with porters and carcases everywhere. It does amaze me that we are allowed to go out and about in our uniforms, complete with aprons, and then we go straight back on the ward.

31 JANUARY: Sunday
Another walk into the night. At 11.48 p.m., during our 'lunch' break, six of us decided to go to St Paul's to hear the new month in. Six nurses running for all their worth – we disregarded the rule that running was allowed only in cases of fire and haemorrhage – towards the Cathedral. We arrived just as the clock struck 12 and we sank down exhausted on the steps, collapsing with laughter. The City of London was very quiet.

3 FEBRUARY: Wednesday
Beth and I are spending our four nights off in Cambridge visiting the two Johns [O. and W.] and Simon H. I have never, ever seen so many men. They are everywhere. I don't think university life would suit me – it is so disorganised and casual. It seems that students roll up to lectures as and when they feel like it.

We are staying in a very good B and B and are zooming around on hired bikes. The Colleges are magnificent and together with the blue sky and the daffodils make the whole place magical. Beth and I cooked lunch for eight or so boys today – they were most impressed.

SECTION I—*(continued)*.	3						
	Surgical		Medical		Paedia-tric	Gynaeco-logical	Class instruc-tion.
	Male	Female	Male	Female			
General care of patient *(continued)*:—							
Taking and charting:	X 8K .						
temperature, pulse, respiration ..							.
Bedmaking:—							
General bedmaking	X 8K .						I
Making children's cots		X NuS					
Special modifications for:							
admission of patient	X 8K .						I
operation/s	X 8K .						I
cardiac diseases				X NuR			I
pulmonary diseases				X NuR			I
fracture/s	X nfs						I
plaster	X nfs						I
Filling and placing hot water bottles				X NuR			I
Use of: water pillows or air pillows	X 8K						
electric pads and blankets ..				X NuR			I
Giving and removing bedpans and urinals	X 8K.						I
Observation, collection of specimens of and disposal of: ..							
urine	X 8K .						I.
faeces	X 8K						I
sputum	X 8K .						I
vomit	X 8K.						I
Measuring and charting fluid intake and output	X 8K.						I
Giving and receiving reports on patients' condition				X NuR			(
Administration of drugs:							
giving medicines	/			X NuR			I
giving hypodermic injections ..				X NuR			(
storage of drugs		X NuS					(
Inhalations:							
steam kettle ..				X NuR			
steam inhaler	X 8K.						I

A practical procedures chart indicated that a nurse had completed a range of specific procedures. The chart was filled in by the ward sister at the end of our time on each ward.

6 FEBRUARY: Saturday
No. I can't bear it – I'm going to leave! Fancy locking the door behind us at 2.30 in the afternoon. Prison must be a joyride compared with this. Don't worry – I'm not really leaving. I just feel better if I say it.

10 FEBRUARY: Wednesday
What a night. Mrs Horwood fell out of bed – she rolled over her bedsides. Imagine. She is so sweet and kept on saying, 'Gawd bless you me deah, Gawd bless you'.

12 FEBRUARY: Friday
Lizzy has had her tracky removed again because it was so sore. Sandy C. (the houseman) gives her four days to get bronchopneumonia again. What is best? Poor Lizzie is so scared and so am I after last time's episode.

13 FEBRUARY: Saturday
I didn't think I would live through tonight – I felt so tired it isn't true. I had completed the usual rounds of bedtime drinks, bedpan duty, cleaning, etc. and by 3 a.m. I was in the ward, which was dark, quiet and quite cold and we are not allowed to even wear a cardigan. Because we were 'on duty' we had two empty beds that were being warmed with electric blankets in readiness to receive any emergencies. I wanted to get into one of those beds so badly it became an obsession. I wondered if I could suddenly be taken ill, but I didn't feel ill – I just desired the warm bed. In the end I went to each bed in turn and put my hands and arms under the covers just to feel the comfort and warmth.

16 FEBRUARY: Tuesday
I hated having to say goodbye to all the patients. They were all so sweet and Sister was pretty complimentary and said she would be giving me a good report. I know I shouldn't want praise and that I should manage without it but it made me feel that the hours of cleaning and giving out bedpan after bedpan were worth it after all. Sister did my chart and now it's four nights off and then off to the ski slopes.

WOMEN'S SURGICAL
Abernethy Ward

Abernethy and Waring firm. The firm that covered these two wards, female and male, was led by two consultants (Mr Naunton Morgan and Mr Ellison Nash). Each ward had its own ward sister as well as surgical registrars and housemen.

7 MARCH: Monday

Well, here we are again, back in Queen Mary's Nurses' Home, fourth floor this time. I'm on Abernethy, which is a Women's Surgical ward. Marvellous. I gather Sister Abernethy is as mad as a hatter and totally disorganised but loved by patients and nurses alike. This is going to be very different from Annie Zunz.

8 MARCH: Tuesday

Abernethy Ward is VERY different and today was an operation day. We had a poor patient who had an abdomino-perineal excision of the rectum, which is a major operation carried out for cancer, and then a list of more minor operations like varicose veins and hernias. All the patients come back from the operating theatre unconscious which is

quite worrying, so we have to watch them very carefully. An artificial airway is in the patient's mouth and when they wake up they tend to spit it out and then vomit.

Mrs Parslow, who is 82 and an old Barts nurse, told us to 'tell that man to get out of my bed – I haven't had a man in bed with me since my husband died!'

11 MARCH: Friday
Black Friday, as Sister so aptly put it. In the middle of the surgeon's round – the famous Mr Naunton Morgan and all his entourage – I managed to spill a whole, full coffee pot all over the floor right in front of everybody. Then, when I picked up the broken lid, I cut my finger. I was so embarrassed. Sister was kindness itself.

24 MARCH: Thursday
I managed to go to the West End in my off duty and had to get a taxi back because I was running late. The taxi fare on the meter read five shillings [25p] but the driver only charged me three. There is a lot of goodwill towards nurses.

Ray Windsor and Anne Tucker, who is sixteen, are both to be operated on by Mr Ellison Nash who is going to do pioneering surgery called ileo-cutaneous ureterostomy. Ray and Anne are both paralysed from the waist down and are incontinent. Mr Nash plans to transplant the ureters onto the intestine and then to bring a small protrusion of the intestine onto the surface of the abdomen so that a bag can be fixed to it to collect the urine.

Ruth [Johnson] who had top marks in our PTS exams (and whose father is an academic) says she is leaving – in fact she has a job lined up already and says she is leaving tomorrow to become a telephonist at £6 4s [£6.20] a week.

Gayle came back to see us tonight for the first time since her midnight flight. She is now a secretary and earning £12 a week.

27 MARCH: Sunday
A very pleasant day off. I managed to get to All Souls Langham Place for both the morning and evening services. All Souls is so inspiring and has very charismatic clergy. John Stott, the Rector is amazing and has a huge student following. The church is always full.

Donald McA. turned up out of the blue so we went out on his Lambretta scooter for a coffee and a flip round London.

We start Study Block tomorrow. I have mixed feelings about going back in the classroom for a month, but it will be good to have every evening off.

Study Block

28 MARCH: Monday
Well, the first day of four weeks' Block is over and it was good, but I prefer ward work.

Helen Collins and Barbara Miller say that they are definitely leaving. Oh dear, how we are dwindling.

29 MARCH: Tuesday
Started psychology today – we are all sure we are 'crazy mixed up kids'.

I had a letter from Ian B. once again asking me to a Commem. Ball at Oxford in June. Maybe I will try and go this time.

I went to the Abernethy Firm Party last night. All the people who presently work on Abernethy were there. I only had to dance once with Brian D. – the houseman – and he asked me if I was doing anything tomorrow night. I suppose he thought a probationer would be flattered to be asked out by the houseman. He was wrong – I'm not going.

1 APRIL: Friday
We were shown how to bath a baby today – I just can't wait to bath my own!

2 APRIL: Saturday
We had a rather disturbed night last night. I was suddenly woken by a bell ringing furiously. At first I thought it was just an ambulance but then I heard another so I leapt out of bed and looked out of the window to see two policemen racing up the road. I flew up to the sixth floor to collect Meg and we

went on the nurses' home roof to see flames pouring out of a window near the new nurses' home which has just been built. We heard a man yelling to someone to get out quickly. Meanwhile the roof of our nurses' home was getting crowded with nurses and sisters – Sister Butlin arrived complete with hairpins and hair net. Firemen put out the fire and we gather all was well – but my, I found it hard to sleep afterwards.

Prissy and I went to watch the Boat Race. Oxford won. Hurrah!

8 APRIL: Friday
I'm endeavouring to work for the inevitable Saturday morning test, I'm not winning.

I went to Abernethy tonight to see Anne Tucker. She is such a lovely girl and so very brave. Wearing nappies and big

bloomers all the time must be dreadful.
I can't wait to get back on the ward.

11 APRIL: Monday

Just heard that Anne has got infective
hepatitis and so can't have the operation
at the moment. She was all prepared, after
having some nasty pre-op procedures, when
the whole thing was called off.

We started Surgery (with Mr Todd) and
Medicine (with Dr Spence) today. We are so
fortunate to have such eminent consultants
to teach us.

13 APRIL: Wednesday

Miss Winifed Hector, the Senior Nurse Tutor
at Barts, is in charge of our Block and is
a great character with a very dry sense of
humour. She told us today that when she
is not at work she never lets anyone know
she is a nurse. 'If I'm asked what I do, I say
I work in the city. If they inquire further, I
reply that I work for a very old firm.' She
also told us that when she was on holiday
in the Greek Islands last year she was 'the
botany mistress from Cheltenham Ladies'
College and so I answered questions on
orchids not prostates'.

14 APRIL: Thursday

Matron read my reports to me today; they
were moderate to good. During our practical
class today Miss Bailey, one of our tutors,
said I would have failed my practical exam
three times over. A bit worrying considering
I have my State Preliminary Practical exam
in six weeks.

I went to see Lizzy this evening, she seems
quite a lot better.

15 APRIL: Good Friday

A crowd of us went to hear the 'Messiah' at
the Royal Albert Hall. It was conducted by
Sir Malcolm Sargent and was wonderful.

19 APRIL: Tuesday

Another gem from Miss Hector to someone
in our set: 'My dear child, if the popliteal
artery ran down the front of the leg, every
day you knelt down to say your prayers,
your feet would go gangrenous.'

There hasn't been a cloud in the sky all
day. How I pine for the country and the
fields. How lucky we are though to have the
Square, at least there is always somewhere
to sit outside and it is never boring.

22 APRIL: Friday

Hurrah! Back to the wards tomorrow. There
is a new 'belt' policy. First year nurses (pros)
are going to wear grey belts, second year a
striped belt and third year a white belt. This
makes a lot of sense because it is difficult
at the moment to tell second and third year
nurses apart because both wear a white belt.
We will have to go backwards and change
our striped belt for a grey one for a couple
of months. The fourth year nurses, known as
'belts', will continue to wear navy belts with
a buckle. Senior staff nurses, called 'pinks',
wear a lovely long-sleeved, pink dress with
cuffs and a flowing cap. Sisters are dressed
in a long-sleeved, royal blue dress and a
longer flowing cap.

For 'barrier nursing', to avoid spreading serious infection from patient to patient, we had to 'gown up' and wear masks and also scrub our hands very thoroughly before and after we attended a patient. All barrier nursing was carried out in an isolated area.

23 APRIL: Saturday
I knew it would be good to be back and it was. My goodness though my feet and ankles ache. It is amazing how much difference Block makes when you get back on the ward – you begin to have a greater overall interest and understanding and soon we will be pros. no longer.

My feet are killing me – I just don't know where to put them to make them comfortable. I've even tried putting the end of my bed on my laundry basket.

25 APRIL: Monday
Ray had her major op. – ileo bladder – today. She came back to the ward in a very good condition. She really is marvellous – imagine, she has already been in this ward for 8 months.

26 APRIL: Tuesday
Ray continues to improve. I was 'promoted' to a 'stripe' this evening and didn't do any 'pro-ing'. I must admit it was very satisfactory.

27 APRIL: Wednesday
Anne Tucker is back on the ward so we can start all the preparations again. She is truly amazing. We have had to put three patients on 'barrier nursing' because of resistant staphylococci – it has caused havoc because we have to gown up before we do anything for them.

2 MAY: Monday
Mr Nash decided at the last minute that he wouldn't do Anne's operation today because Ray, who had the operation last week, has become very ill with an intestinal obstruction. Poor Anne had got herself all prepared for the second time – enemas, hyperclonic washouts and pill preparations. She and I had been so joyful when I removed her nappy for what we thought would be the last time.

4 MAY: Wednesday
A year ago today! Yes, we have been here 366 days (it's a leap year). I just cannot believe it. I have never known a year go by so quickly. Do I have any regrets? Absolutely none.

8 MAY: Sunday
Ray is terribly ill again. Her parents are with her. She just mustn't die. I feel so sorry for poor Anne who is having the same operation tomorrow.

Miss Barton died early this morning. She was 74 and a former missionary and matron. She was adorable, very cantankerous but so lovable. Yesterday as I fed her she kept praying aloud ending with, 'He is my strength and my Redeemer'. As I left, she said, 'God Bless You'. I was sure then that it would be the last time I would speak to her.

9 MAY: Monday
Ray is very slightly better but one foot is still blue and the crater (bedsore) which she has named Dracula is dreadful, worse than it ever was and right through to the sacrum. Anne has at last had her operation. She even managed a smile when she got back from Theatre.

11 MAY: Wednesday
View Day. The Square looks very smart. Geraniums abound and the tops of the shelters have been painted and the lamps cleaned with the aid of a bladder syringe.

Today was special and wonderfully traditional. View Day always happens on the second Wednesday in May and was instituted in the 1700s as an annual tour of inspection by the Lord Mayor of London, various dignitaries and benefactors. It's also the day when the hospital is open to the general public.

Sister Abernethy and the other ward sisters went off early to Covent Garden to buy flowers for their wards and we put on a sumptuous tea for the visitors. The Governors, Matron, and senior Medical Consultants – all dressed in morning dress, went in formal procession to inspect the hospital and us. Although we had a job to get ready in time we all managed to look very spick, span and crisp in our uniform.

My parents and Prissy's parents joined us and were 'our' distinguished and proud visitors.

View Day at Barts, when the hospital was shown off to the public. Everywhere had to be immaculate and the Square was a picture with geraniums in abundance. Everyone was at their smartest, with many of the men in morning suits.

13 MAY: Friday

This morning Sister didn't think Ray would last the day and had to tell her parents and she asked me to go and comfort them – they are so upset. She went down to Theatre again this afternoon and her condition is still very critical.

Anne is now out of the critical stage and is much improved. We have decided to call her spout 'Elly' after Mr Ellison Nash the surgeon.

20 MAY: Friday

Oh dear, one of those days. Between 12.30 and 1.30 p.m. I was told off continually. I knocked over some screens, I carried a bedpan so it touched my apron and I put four bedpans on top of a commode to convey them to the various patients, all to the disgust of the 'pink' and 'belt'.

Thank goodness Ray's condition has improved and she looks considerably better.

View Day Ceremony, which included a tour of inspection by the Lord Mayor of London, the Hospital Governors, Matron and the senior medical consultants.
The mothers of Prissy and Greta chatting with us and each other.

22 MAY: Sunday

Anne walked to the table and back again today. Somehow when she is in bed you forget how disabled she is. She tried so hard and she is such a plucky girl. Ray continues to improve – she even managed a yogurt.

We went to see the historic Ceremony of the Keys this evening at the Tower of London.

24 MAY: Tuesday

Poor Meg was sent home today until Friday – she is very run down and didn't go to sleep until 5.0 a.m. this morning.

At last I have done some studying. I must try and make myself realise that the second part of the written Preliminary Exam (I'm exempt from the first part because I passed 'O' level Human Biology) is next Tuesday.

27 MAY: Friday

Meg came back today but she doesn't seem much better.

31 MAY: Tuesday

Well, another exam done but probably not finished with. It was awful.

1 JUNE: Wednesday

Anne went home today. We shall miss her.

I had a letter from Michael W. today, asking me out to supper on Friday. I'm going to break my pact – I said I wouldn't go out with a medical student – but we are definitely 'just good friends'.

Flowers brightened up the wards during the day but had to be removed each night as carbon dioxide given off in the dark was considered harmful. I also found that red and white flowers were never put together as some patients believed this combination heralded death.

3 JUNE: Friday

Quite a pleasant evening with Michael – nothing special.

Abernethy was absolutely frantic. Nearly everyone had to be washed and there were loads of big dressings. However it is great fun – we all seem to be working together as a team.

Two quotes we heard today from Mr Naunton Morgan: 'Where there is wind there is a way,' and 'What sounds obnoxious to a duchess sounds like music in a surgeon's ear,' (i.e., flatus).

8 JUNE: Wednesday

Thank goodness the practical exam is over. Besides other things, we had to do a steam tent, where the sheet has to be fixed over two screens. The sheet was so small it fell on top of the 'patient'. I peeped under the sheet and there he lay killing himself with laughter. He then put his finger in his mouth and 'hollored' (quietly) like a Red Indian.

10 JUNE: Friday

A day off and breakfast in bed. Roes on toast, which I don't like, but just being served breakfast in bed is such a treat. Somehow I think it's a way of showing us how we should look after our patients.

13 JUNE: Monday

I went up to see Lizzy in my off duty. She is so miserable and depressed.

17 JUNE: Friday

A really enjoyable morning on the ward. I had to do all the big dressings as there were no 'stripes' on duty. I have very sadly left Abernethy, my favourite ward to date, due I think to Sister and the way she cares for her patients.

Well, I did go to the Commem. Ball at Oxford with Ian B. Quite an occasion. A cocktail party at Trinity College first, then dinner at University College and dancing to two bands in a huge marquee. It was glorious weather and at 4.30 a.m. we went punting. I don't know whether I want to go to another one but it was certainly an experience.

2 JULY: Saturday

Back from holidaying in Sandbanks. I'm going on to Theatres next Thursday and then on Night Duty there on the 16th. Until Thursday, I'm on Annie for a few days.

Great news, we've gone into our striped belts (again!). No longer are we 'pros'. Not that this has made much difference to my day – there are no pros. on the ward and I am back at the bedpans and making sure all the flowers are removed from the ward before the night staff arrive.

Operating Theatres

The swab counting rack was very necessary in the operating theatre to ensure that all swabs were accounted for and so would not be left inside a patient.

7 JULY: Thursday
This is something different. I was petrified. I'm on Theatre D and it was like starting our training all over again. Party dresses, stills, tobies…. It is like a foreign language and means nothing to me.

We have to change our shoes, wear a theatre frock instead of our uniform, cover our hair completely and wear a mask which must never be touched by the fingers once it has been put on. All this is called getting dressed in 'greens', simply because everything is green.

I was just an observer today so I kept well out of the way of everyone. Apart from viewing several operations, I noticed that afternoon tea is served in the theatre ante room for all theatre staff, surgeons and nurses alike and, would you believe, it was delicious? All sorts of different sandwiches and all with their crusts cut off. Very jolly.

At the end of the list, when all the instruments had been sterilised and were being counted, it was found that a towel clip was missing. Panic! We searched for an hour and a half – I was given the dirty and bloody linen to check – before it was found in its rightful place but had become tucked under another clip so it could not be seen.

10 JULY: Sunday
What a day, nothing has gone right! Everything that could go wrong did go wrong and I managed to contaminate everything in sight. There were no operations in our theatre but there was still the cleaning, sterilising, and the laying up of trolleys.

13 JULY: Wednesday
I suddenly found myself enjoying theatres. Everything is beginning to click into place like a well oiled machine. I have been trying to learn the names of instruments: the various forceps, needle holders, clamps, etc.

14 JULY: Thursday
No operations. A day spent cleaning. Doors polished, brasses cleaned, all the cupboards cleared out and solutions replaced in neat rows – large bottles at the back and all the labels facing forward – as we were taught at PTS. Finally, there were the lavatories to be scrubbed.

A good day.

18 JULY: Monday
The days seem to roll by regardless. We continue to dish up and clear up!

20 JULY: Wednesday
Helen and Pat both gave in their notice today. We will be down to 25.

22 JULY: Friday
There is a very good atmosphere on Theatre D and there is a lot of good-humoured banter. The gorgeous Mr Todd wasn't too happy today though when the houseman was meant to be running fluid into a patient's rectum: 'That should be going into the rectum not on my feet, man!'

Beacher, the orderly, put a cold ether swab down my back and as I ran away he stuck his foot out and I tripped onto the concrete floor. Short-lived agony and a large bruise, but a good laugh.

An operating theatre. The powerful lights were directed over the operating site. In the foreground are 'tobies', bowls on wheels used for collecting soiled items.

24 JULY: Sunday
Two pieces of good news today.
First, I managed to pass the second part of my Preliminary Examination – in spite of the fiasco with the steam tent – and second, I scrubbed for my first case, which was a burns case.

26 JULY: Tuesday
We didn't get off duty until 9.50 this evening. We had a very busy operating day and I was told off by the Theatre Superintendent (known as Belinda) for having 'dirty hands'. She marched into the theatre, came straight up to me and said she had seen me touch a lamp. I had to go and wash my hands like a schoolchild.

29 JULY: Friday
I'm really getting into the swing of theatres. I 'took' several cases today and was to have taken the whole list but unfortunately had to come off duty before the surgeons had finished.

Sir James Paterson Ross came into the theatre today and opened the door for me; what a gentleman.

"...some nurses complain that they have to dust and sweep and do other household work, which could be more quickly and efficiently performed by less well-educated women.... If it be true, as we are taught in these days, that absolute cleanliness is a most essential factor in the recovery of a patient,... then, I think, that housemaids' work is an important part of a nurse's training, and that nurse only is efficient who can clean a room so deftly and well as not to disturb her patient....the best nurses,... in realizing the necessity of cleanliness, do not wish to escape from the occasional hardness implied by it."

The virtues of cleaning as described by Isla Stewart in an article in 'Murray's Magazine', August 1890. Isla Stewart was Matron of Barts from 1887 to 1910. Her words were as relevant to us as they were in her day.

31 JULY: Sunday
I spent six hours cleaning the theatre.

Meg is upset and is determined to leave, and yesterday her mother agreed she could. However, when she spoke to her father today, he said she should carry on. Prissy had also made up her mind to leave but, after talking to HER parents, has decided to stay on for the moment.

9 AUGUST: Tuesday
The porters seem to have nothing better to do than report late nurses. It was my turn today because I was half an hour late in on Sunday.

12 AUGUST: Friday
Three months of night duty. Well, at least the lights are on. We had three duty cases which meant the men didn't finish until 1 a.m. and they are not only on call but will have to be on the ward early in the morning.

Cleaning, cleaning, cleaning. There are two junior nurses on duty at a time – Frances (Carpenter), Jackie (Roberts) and I rotate – as well as a 'pink' or a sister on call. We juniors have to go round all the theatres in the hospital washing the walls with long-handled mops and laying 'sides' in readiness for the next day. It is quite eerie working in a theatre on your own at night and having to get changed into sterile 'greens' in each different theatre. If an operation is in progress during the early hours of the morning, one junior has to do all the theatres while the other attends the operation.

17 AUGUST: Wednesday
A lesson on how to 'take' an appendicectomy tonight. Helen Jolly (the 'pink') was our tutor. We laid up the trolley, took it to the operating table and pretended the patient was on the table all towelled up. We were set for the off when in came Sandy C., the houseman, who has taken a shine for Helen and she for him. Although we asked him if he would like to pose as the patient, he declined with horror but reappeared and put a jelly baby on our 'site' ready for us to operate. Learning can be such fun.

19 AUGUST: Friday
It was all fairly quiet until 9.30 p.m. Then we had a D. and C., which, although I had never even seen one before, I had to take for Mr Bourne, the Gynaecology and Obstetrics Registrar. He never stopped teasing me about my brown back as he could see my tan through the openings of my 'party dress'. I blushed under my mask.

Miss Hearne, the 'pink', left to go to bed. Frances and I were left to do the chores struggling to keep awake. By 7.20 a.m. we had finished and had changed into our uniform when the telephone rang. 'Mr Abercrombie here. Caesar in 10 minutes.' I said, 'You are joking'. He wasn't. PANIC. Frances and I looked at each other in amazement, horror, amusement and incredulity. We threw off our uniform, got into green again and woke Miss Hearne. I flew off to Theatre A, which is the Gynae. Theatre, to put the instruments in the boiler. Suddenly the operating theatre was a beehive of activity. Unshaven men arrived in their pyjamas, Miss Hearne appeared and the patient was wheeled in. All in 10 minutes. A few seconds later, a slimy, blue but beautiful little girl came into this world. What a miracle.

Operation in progress. The theatre sister and nurses wore 'party dresses' with gym shoes on their feet. It was important to be able to think and react quickly and also to enjoy teamwork.

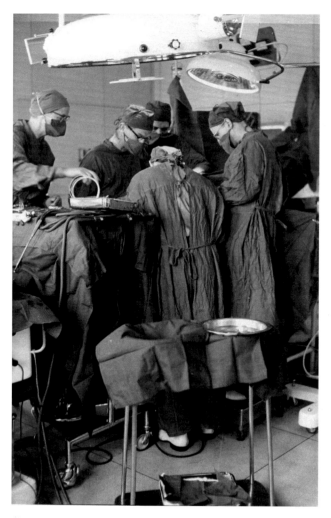

24 AUGUST: Wednesday

I made a big boob tonight. One of the theatre floors needed a special clean, so I phoned John, the orderly. I was quite sure the number was 305, so, large as life, I phoned that number. Is that you John?' 'Yes.' 'Could you come and clean the theatre floor please?' There was then a long pause at the end of the phone. Had I got the wrong number? I had. The man's name was John all right but he was the senior pathologist. I was covered in confusion and I'm still trying to live it down.

I was right about Helen and Sandy. I was waiting for the lift and as the doors opened who were having an embrace but those two!

26 AUGUST: Friday

What a dreadful day! Beth had to go to have a repeat X-ray of her chest this morning. I kept waiting for her to come back, feeling that perhaps something was wrong. At 6 p.m. I went to find Miss Lomax, the Warden, who informed me that Beth was going to be off for at least six months as she had 'shadows on both lungs'. I just can't believe it. Six months. We went to see her tonight – she was cheerful but I don't really think the truth has hit her. This nursing business is pretty hazardous.

29 AUGUST: Monday

Beth is warded on Annie Zunz and has to have three gastric lavages.

1 SEPTEMBER: Thursday

Beth's final lavage. The first two were negative so here's hoping.

8 SEPTEMBER: Thursday

The weather looks gorgeous and I've got to go to bed. Quick, draw the curtains!

12 SEPTEMBER: Monday

We eventually got our lunch at 4 a.m. First, we had an ectopic pregnancy, and then a baby from Kenton Ward who had had a cardiac arrest at 7 p.m. and had to be opened up again on the ward at 1.15 a.m. As both the 'twilight' and Miss Acres had gone off duty, I was left to be 'belt'. The Paediatric Registrar just phoned up and seemed to think I would know what sort of trolley to prepare. The poor wee mite – this time they opened him up they found a punctured lung. We left the ward at 2.30 a.m. and the babe died at 2.45 a.m. I suppose it was for the best, but it was so sad.

18 SEPTEMBER: Sunday

We had another ten minute caesar. The phone rang: 'Nurse, caesar in ten minutes.' Me: 'Er yes, who is going to do it?' Pause. 'Angela Gaddam.' Shrieks of laughter. 'I'll get her!'

I went to see Beth on the ward and rubbed her back, or rather bottom, so she wouldn't get bed sores.

19 SEPTEMBER: Monday

We operated, under a local anaesthetic, on a little old man of ninety (Mr Campbell), who had a strangulated hernia. He had recently retired from working at the Arsenal football ground and was in such high spirits, telling us one story after another. I was holding his hand so I got all the asides too. At one point, Mr Bliss had to put his instruments down because he just couldn't carry on for laughing. It all became more and more riotous and in the end the two anaesthetists put ice down my back for good measure.

22 SEPTEMBER: Thursday

It's hard to believe that the sordid things one reads about in the papers really happen. We carried out a D. and C. on a girl of 21 who had tried to carry out a criminal abortion on herself by using potassium permanganate. She didn't realise that it made one bleed not abort. There is another sad case at the moment on Harley Ward. A woman has gas gangrene from attempting an abortion under pressure from her husband.

She is 31 and dreadfully ill.

23 SEPTEMBER: Friday

The poor woman who had gas gangrene has died. We gather she was having the baby by a man other than her husband – her husband had been away in the navy. When he heard the news on his homecoming, they agreed to try and make a go of it but only if she got rid of the baby. What a dreadful conclusion it all came to – she had three other children who now have no mother.

1 OCTOBER: Saturday

I met Walter M. for coffee this morning at the Cumberland Hotel. It was good to meet up.

I've just heard that Lizzie [in Annie Zunz Ward] has pneumonia again which is very worrying.

2 OCTOBER: Sunday

An extra hour's work due to British Summer Time ending and only four hours sleep yesterday. I'm feeling whacked.

Dear Mr Campbell, the old man whose hernia we operated on under local anaesthetic, died this morning. Bless him. I'm sure he died happy.

4 OCTOBER: Tuesday

A short night. We had an abundance of visitors. Also one operation carried out by Harvey Ross (Sir James Paterson Ross's son) who is a new registrar. He is rather gorgeous and great fun.

6 OCTOBER: Thursday

Operated all night. We had to cover two theatres that had not finished the day cases. Then we had a suspected strangulated hernia, which turned out to be a resection of the gut for cancer and took three hours, as well as having to dry the instruments, clear up and start the next round of getting theatres ready for the morning. We had a cup of soup at 3 a.m. and then some cornflakes and bread and butter at 5 a.m., our total sum of food in 12 hours.

14 OCTOBER: Friday

Another heavy night. I scrubbed for several ops and then it was back to the cleaning. At 2.30 a.m. we had to start the round as we had to wall wash, dust and sterilise in all the theatres. There were five sides to lay up.

Ormy [Miss Ormeston, the Sickrooms Sister] has put a bottle of multivitamins in each theatre as she is worried that many nurses who work there are off sick or feeling ropey. We have to take them twice a day.

I had a letter from Anne Tucker [who was in Abernethy Ward] today who seems remarkably fit and well.

25 OCTOBER: Tuesday

Great drama, a cousin of Mr Nash has been admitted and required an emergency operation for a chronic subdural haematoma. Mr Campbell Connolly, the neurosurgeon, was summoned from Hill End and he performed a burr holes and excavation of the haematoma which was really horrible to watch. The Superintendent of Theatres, of course, took the case.

29 OCTOBER: Saturday

What a night! We didn't sit down from the moment we came on until the moment we got off.

Surgeons using their skills to carry out an operation. However, a successful operation also depended on the whole team comprising theatre sister, nurses and orderlies.

We arrived to find we had a query strangulated hernia which turned out to be a gonorrhoeal infection – it was horrible. Then we had a poor little woman with carcinomatosis who had to have a colostomy raised. Her operation had been scheduled for 2.30 p.m. but as the day list had run on the surgeons were not ready for her until 9.30 p.m. She only has a prognosis of about a month. After this, Garfield D. (the houseman) and I scrubbed up for an appendicectomy. Then, just as we were getting the patient off the table, the phone rang and we had a caesar to perform. This was all blamed on me because I said I wanted another caesar before I left theatres. What a rush – we hadn't even done the round and had to have two extra nurses to give us a hand. We did not eat ANYTHING between 7.30 p.m. and 8.0 a.m. the next morning. It was a very exciting night – but golly it was exhausting.

30 OCTOBER: Sunday

I saw my first grafting last night; the skin was taken from a man's leg and grafted on to the forearm. According to the patient he had been drunk and had fallen asleep on his bed. He had woken up to the smell of burning flesh and had found that the electric fire near his bed had burnt him. He then went for another drink before coming to hospital. The burn looked horrible, all black and charred.

31 OCTOBER: Monday

I'm off night duty. Hurrah! I gather I have to come back to theatres for several days before I go on Rahere Ward.

MEN'S MEDICAL
Rahere Ward

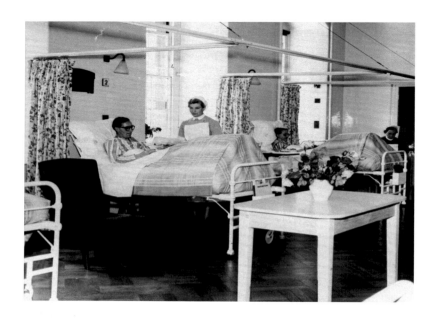

A nurse looks after a patient's needs. Medical wards were typically less lively than surgical wards as many patients were suffering from terminal disease, although the word cancer was not mentioned.

7 NOVEMBER: Monday
It feels part of history to be working on Rahere Ward, for it was the monk Rahere who, in 1123 AD, founded the Augustinian Priory and St Bartholomew's Hospital. It is said that Rahere went on a pilgrimage to Rome where he fell ill. Thinking he would die, he vowed that if he recovered he would return home and found a hospital for the poor. He did recover and on his way back is supposed to have seen a vision of St Bartholomew who told him to build his hospital in Smithfield; and here we are over 800 years later and still going strong!

It's wonderful to be back on a ward at last. My goodness though it is amazing how much I have forgotten. What a change from 'pro-ing'. We admitted a dear old man as a 'duty case' today who died just as I was about to wash him. Although there were three doctors and two nurses trying to save his life there was nothing we could do. The man had an infarction and was so mystified by it all but he was so brave.

I'll never go back to theatres as a 'belt' if I can possibly help it - give me a ward any day.

10 NOVEMBER: Thursday
I heard the hymn and short story programme on the radio this morning. It was about the founding of Barts. I couldn't believe it, I felt so proud.

14 NOVEMBER: Monday
We have been very slack over the last few days. But this morning it was a different story. Sister didn't stop shouting and there was a great panic

Grant by the monk Rahere.
Dating from 1137, this is the oldest
document in the hospital archives.
It was sealed in the presence of
Rahere and has remained in the
hospital ever since.

Weekend breakfasts of scrambled
or boiled eggs were cooked by the
day nurses. Sometimes we muddled
the orders but the patients didn't
seem to mind too much and never
told on us.

over a needle she was sure I had mislaid which in reality had been taken
by the syringe service woman. Anyway we parted the best of friends,
with her saying, 'Now off you go and have a good day off what's left of
you'. I found to my horror this afternoon that I had forgotten to sign the
drug book.

16 NOVEMBER: Wednesday
It's always difficult to come back after a day off. But the men are
always so appreciative and after their welcome I felt it wouldn't really
matter if I never had another day off. Sister is still very 'toxic' but
she is rather gorgeous.

Yet another member of our set left today. Carol Harvey has got
engaged to one of the medical students. She plans to get married next
summer and has decided to call it a day.

17 NOVEMBER: Thursday
Judy Edwards from our set has cut her wrist very badly. She fell on a
bottle of blood of all things and severed a nerve, artery and tendon. She
was warded immediately and taken to theatre so Mr Nash could operate.
It's her birthday and none of us knew. Luckily we found out and have
bought her a nightdress. She has been told she will be off sick for at
least three months but we wonder whether she will come back as she is
not at all fond of nursing.

20 NOVEMBER: Sunday
Well, if I ever want to be an air hostess on BOAC I'm fixed. A very big
bug from the airline who works in Washington said today he would pull
strings for me. It's certainly a way of seeing the world.

I don't think I have mentioned that we have to cook breakfast for the
patients at the weekend. We can cook boiled and scrambled eggs to
perfection, but remembering who has which is another matter.

There was a late night party last night and apparently one of the
nurses went to Snowhill Police Station and asked one of the sergeants to
go back with her to give her a lift over the mortuary gates and into the
Square. He obliged with pleasure.

21 NOVEMBER: Monday
At long last I managed to go back to Abernethy for Sister to complete
my chart. No sooner had I got there when she asked me to go out
and buy some mushrooms as she wanted to tempt a patient to eat by
cooking her chips, eggs and mushrooms.

Two of us had quite a fight with Mr Medcalf, a pillar of society, this
afternoon as he had a hypoglycaemic attack. We had to give him

intravenous glucose as he wouldn't take glucose by mouth. He shouted and screamed and clutched us as we tried to get his coat off. When he was improving he pinched a piece of cake off the trolley which he knew he was not allowed – I managed to grab the remaining half out of his hand much to his disgust.

26 NOVEMBER: Saturday
Soon after I got back today from my day off Mr Martin, a lovely patient, died. Apparently he was feeling better yesterday and even got up for tea but his condition deteriorated during the night. It was a very quiet death and he looked so peaceful. As I looked at him it was hard to believe that such a short time ago he always used to exclaim, 'Oh Nurse are ALL those pills for me?' in such a tone of pleasure and gratitude.

1 DECEMBER: Thursday
Mr Martin's family sent all the nurses on Rahere a beautiful bunch of violets. We were very touched.

5 DECEMBER: Monday
I washed the dirtiest pair of feet yet today. They were FILTHY – the poor man hadn't been able to bend down to wash them because of his chest. He said that if he had known he was coming into hospital he would have gone out for a bath. Imagine not having a bath at your disposal. I gather he hadn't taken his socks off for a month and had to get a friend down the road to undo his shoes. It took me over three quarters of an hour just to wash his feet and cut his horny toenails. Two years ago I would have been horrified and disgusted. It is so different now because I understand why he couldn't keep clean and find it perfectly acceptable.

6 DECEMBER: Tuesday
I went on an errand for Sister today in my off duty. I bought 18 puzzles, 18 pieces of soap, and 18 combs for the men's Christmas stockings. I hope her calculations are right as we have 26 beds. I suppose she is banking on the numbers being reduced over the festive season.

   I have just heard that Lizzie has been transferred from Annie Zunz to another hospital, miles away from here, but nearer to her relatives. I haven't been able to say goodbye.

7 DECEMBER: Wednesday
Meg and I climbed to the very top of St Paul's Cathedral this afternoon. Yes, to the very top. All for nothing as it's free for Barts nurses.

   Carol popped in this evening and said she plans to get married at the

St. Bartholomew's Hospital

Rahere WARD 7. 12. 1960
E. R. Tisdale. is granted
Leave of Absence from 8 pm until 12 midnight

J. K. Loveridge.
Matron and
Superintendent of Nursing.

Time of { Going out..............
{ Return ....

Nurses with late passes must be booked in: Smithfield Gate,
10.30 p.m.–12 midnight. Giltspur Gate, after midnight

St Paul's Cathedral has a lot of
steps to climb in order to reach the
stone gallery under the dome, but
what a wonderful view of London
there is on arrival.
Late pass. Although we were
allowed two late passes a week until
12 midnight, we rarely used both
because we felt too tired.

end of May or early June next year at Barts
the Great. Yet another lovely tradition where
staff from Barts are allowed to marry in the
larger church outside the walls of the hospital
which was also founded by Rahere.

Used a late pass to go to the theatre as I knew
I wouldn't be back by 10.30.

12 DECEMBER: Monday
Beth has come up to see Dr Oswald. She looks
so well and positively blooming. Guess what?
The 'Powers that Be' are sending her to Davos in Switzerland. She will
be staying in a hotel with all her expenses paid by Barts. It's a good
time of the year to be going. The ski-ing is excellent in Davos!

19 DECEMBER: Monday
Two new pros. came on the ward for their first visit. They are so green.
Were WE ever like that?

I've managed to buy a very pretty dress for Matron's Ball. It's
organza, pink and white candy stripes with gold woven into the white.

The medical students are being very attentive in the hope we will
invite them to the Ball. Lovely girls, free dinner and drink and a first
class band. What more could they want? We are keeping them guessing.

23 DECEMBER: Friday
Christmas is drawing closer. The whole hospital is bustling with
activity. Pianos are lined up in the 'Colostomy' [the main hospital
corridor leading from the Square], Christmas trees are in abundance and

the wards are beginning to look very festive.

Poor Mr Reider who has cancer of the stomach is going downhill very fast. He can keep nothing down and vomits everything back within seconds. He is very cheerful and says that all he wants to do is to die – and that he might just as well because after all everyone has to sometime. He, of course, doesn't know he has cancer.

Carol singing by the nurses. We started in the Great Hall and then all the wards were visited. It was a very special and emotional occasion for the patients and the nurses.

24 DECEMBER: Saturday

There is a mad rush to get everywhere decorated in time. The ward is looking lovely. We are ready to compete with all the other wards for the best decorated nurses' caps. We have attached red ribbon to the band of our caps and then sewn on mistletoe, holly and small bells to the ribbon.

Sister Rahere and Sister Colston (from the female ward opposite Rahere) gave all their nurses and medical students a tea party today. This was held in the corridor area between the two wards. The Sisters were marvellous. They wouldn't let us do a thing to help.

We dashed back on the ward for the evening duties and then many of us went round the hospital to the candlelit wards carol singing. Our cloaks were turned inside out so we appeared to be wearing Christmassy scarlet. The patients were very touched and tears were never far away.

We went to Midnight Communion at All Souls Langham Place which was packed. About half the congregation were nurses in their various hospital uniforms. Off then back to Barts to have our own present giving and receiving session in Anne's room. Bed at 3.30 a.m.

25 DECEMBER: Sunday

Merry Christmas! A lovely, very hard working Christmas Day but with no off duty. We have 23 patients so I hope Sister bought some more stocking gifts.

All the student nurses who were working on day duty were given a special Christmas Lunch which was served to us rather than the usual self service. Melon, turkey with all the trimmings, Christmas pudding, mince pies and fruit. There was much laughter and everyone looked very gay in their differently decorated headgear.

At 12.30 p.m. we rushed into the Square – about 150 of us – and sang 'Auld Lang Syne' round the Fountain. Father Christmas (Malcolm Evans, the anaesthetist) was spied and he was dragged to the Fountain and thrown in. He was drenched! Sir James Paterson Ross was walking across the Square at the time and was heard to say that he had never seen such a marvellous sight since he started at Barts.

Back to the ward at 1 p.m. to serve the patients their Christmas Lunch, with the turkey carved by one of the ward's consultants.

Turkeys being prepared for the oven by a member of the kitchen staff. Consultants came on to the wards to carve the birds for the patients' traditional Christmas lunch. **Christmas cakes** being decorated. Each ward had its own decorated cake which was enjoyed by the patients, their visitors and the staff.

Visitors in the afternoon and merriment. Hard work in the evening because we have a lot of very sick patients and finally a coffee party in Frances' room at 9 p.m. We were all exhausted but happy – twelve and a half hours on duty in the daytime seems much longer than at night.

26 DECEMBER: Monday
Today, ward shows were put on by the medical students from each firm. Our firm (Rahere and Colston) put on an excellent performance but the best was from the Out Patient boys doing a skit using the music from 'West Side Story'. They brought the house down with 'Tight as a Tick at the Grosvenor'.

We made tea again for all the consultants and their wives and families and by this evening were beginning to feel a little jaded until we got our second wind and went to Matron's Christmas Party, which wasn't very inspiring. In fact we left early and went to see Meg who is on night duty on Lucas, one of the children's wards. The children looked so sweet fast asleep and the ward was beautifully decorated. Bed at 1 a.m.

28 DECEMBER: Wednesday
Sister thanked us yet again for working so hard. My goodness if we worked hard I don't know what she did.

We admitted a very sick patient this evening who is a Roman Catholic

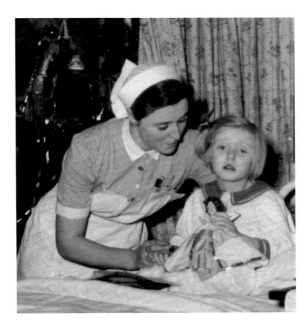

The Christmas stocking was a highlight, especially for the children whose stockings were filled with toys. The adults had more mundane, useful gifts such as soap and combs. **A Christmas doll** is clutched by a sick child tended by a nurse.

and his family asked that he should have the last rites. We were busy with the patient when the priest arrived and so we had to keep him waiting for a few minutes. Suddenly I heard the priest say, 'I wish they would hurry up I want to get back in time to see "Wagon Train" on the television'. I was speechless.

Later, we all went to watch the 'potpourri', where all the medical students' shows are put on at one big performance. It was hilarious.

31 DECEMBER: Saturday
The last day of 1960. What a wonderful year it has been, probably the happiest year of my life yet.

3 JANUARY: Tuesday
Excitement for Matron's Ball at the Grosvenor mounts.

4 JANUARY: Wednesday
Anna [Nowakowska] and I went to have our hair done and a manicure (yes!). Neither of us has ever had a manicure before, so it was a new experience. We felt a million as we left the salon. We were due to meet the boys at 9 p.m. when at 8.55 p.m. calamity struck. Anna's zip broke. Fortunately we found a friendly pro. who sewed Anna into her gown. The Ball was a very grand affair in a very grand hotel. We had decided

55

Matron's Ball at the Grosvenor House Hotel in Mayfair was a very grand occasion. Here, Anna, on the right, and I are enjoying ourselves with my brother between us.

to go in a group rather than as couples but each nurse had to apply for two tickets so it looked as if we had a partner. I felt guilty dancing the last waltz with Stewart, a Scot in a swinging kilt, because Pam [Page] had invited him and I think she probably likes him and I'm not interested in him.

After the Ball, 12 of us went to find a place where we could have coffee. We tried Euston Station but the café was shut, then to a smart place but it was too expensive and finally ended up in Mick's Café in Fleet Street which was awash with printers. What a lark! The boys eventually dropped us at Out Patients at 3.30 a.m. and to our surprise the porter let us in without a murmur. We went to see Prissy, who had worked until 2.30 a.m. to cover for a 'party goer', to show her our dresses and we got to bed at 4.30 a.m.

6 JANUARY: Friday
A patient's visitor referred to me as 'Miss' this evening. The patient put him right very firmly. 'She isn't 'Miss', she is a 'Nurse'. Ah well. On thinking about it, it occurs to me that ALL our sisters are Miss and unmarried except I think one sister on Out Patients who is a widow.

9 JANUARY: Monday
Our set has moved from the Nurses' Home at Barts to Maybury Mansions. I don't know about a 'Mansion' but my room is tiny. Not a very good day. I broke a tooth, we had five 'duty cases' in two hours and I didn't get any supper because we were not off in time. Then, to crown it all I was told off by the Maybury warden for taking my bath towel over to Barts and not bringing it back. The wardens in this place are bad-tempered and seem to enjoy telling people off – they never seem to do anything else. To think that we are NEVER allowed to lose OUR tempers.

Dear Mr Reider died this afternoon. I laid him out. This is the first time I've done the actual laying out myself. He looked so peaceful. He'll be happy now.

I can't wait for my holiday. Only three days and we are off ski-ing.

29 JANUARY: Sunday
Help. Here we are back again after a wonderful holiday, lots of sun and snow. Now back to another Study Block. It doesn't seem five minutes since we were last in Block.

Study Block

30 JANUARY: Monday
We are one of the first sets to have
our Study Block in the new Nurses'
Teaching Department, which is in the
top storey of Gloucester House, the new
Nurses' Home. It is wonderfully light
and a big change from the old basement
classrooms. It has an incredible view
looking towards St Paul's.

The new Nurses' Home has lots of facilities including bedsits, a swimming pool and kitchens for the nurses.

I think I omitted to say that I'm going to Hill End after Block. We are meant to be positively the last bunch – but I wonder if we will be. The Queen is opening the new building in May which will house all the Hill End wards, so we will have to be back in London by then.

Carol came to the hospital to see us all. She looks so well and is getting married in 13 weeks. We are all green with envy. She looks as pretty as ever.

6 FEBRUARY: Monday
There is nothing really of interest to write about in Block. It's just Study, Study, Study. I can't wait to get back on the wards.

I saw Beth and she looks very well and is off to Switzerland for her convalescence next Tuesday.

12 FEBRUARY: Sunday
Home for the weekend and tea at the Vicarage which was delicious (fruit salad and cream). Just me, Rev. D. and his mother. I was quite surprised to find that no one else had been invited.

14 FEBRUARY: Tuesday
Shrove Tuesday – Pancake Day. We held a Pancake Party at Maybury Mansions for the set. Such jollity tossing the pancakes.

16 FEBRUARY: Thursday
Now I realise why I was the only one invited

to the Vicarage. I received a 40-sided letter today from Rev. D. as well as a book. He seems to think we have a future together. I had not expected this.

22 FEBRUARY: Wednesday
I'm getting fed up with Block and I'm itching to get back on the wards.

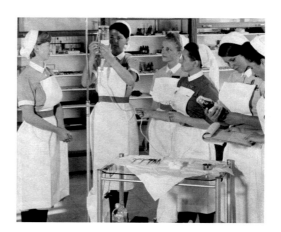

NEUROSURGICAL
Hill End Hospital

24 FEBRUARY: Friday

We didn't know whether to laugh or cry when we arrived. We decided it was probably easier to laugh. Hill End Hospital in St Albans is a very old, large psychiatric hospital which since World War II has housed some of the units from Barts. There are 'miles and miles' of long, straight corridors where many psychiatric patients are either walking up and down or just standing and rocking backwards and forwards; it has to be seen to be believed.

I'm going on Cavell Ward, better known as 'F.C.', which is what it was called before the ward was renamed. It is the neurosurgical ward. I'm really excited because I know this will be 'real' nursing. J.O.C. [John O'Connell], the neurosurgeon is famous because he recently separated the Thackeray Siamese twins, Timothy and Jeremy.

As I write this diary, I can hear umpteen radios blaring forth – the penalty of rooming in cubicles with 30 other women.

The outside of Hill End Hospital in winter. It was such a different environment in which to work: a run down hospital and vermin riddled but such excellent and exciting work with very low infection rates.

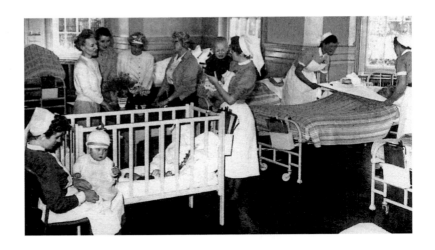

A bustle of activity on the neurosurgical ward. This ward was perhaps the most distressing but rewarding ward I worked on. We worked very long hours with limited equipment and we always felt there was a race against time.

25 FEBRUARY: Saturday

It is very hard to be prepared for this sort of nursing. There are so many patients that are living cabbages but Sister Cavell is remarkable and I can see that the teamwork and camaraderie here play an important role in looking after the patients.

1 MARCH: Wednesday

I'm feeling much more settled and the work is so interesting. The darling children on the ward with brain tumours – it's so sad.

3 MARCH: Friday

I had a lovely day today. I took Lesley aged 8 months up to Barts to be photographed. Her head is swathed in bandages but she was so good. I was in mufti and so everyone thought I was her mother. 'Mummy' – what a lovely thought.

4 MARCH: Saturday

A horrid day. I feel dreadful. There was a misunderstanding over the sterilisation of lumbar puncture sets. Theatres had sent them back to the ward unsterilised and I hadn't noticed and should have done. It was awful. The 'pink', Miss Kay, took me to task, but kindly. It was a big mistake. I'm worried now that a patient may get infected.

6 MARCH: Monday

Instead of sleeping in our off duty, Prissy, Anna and I cycled into St Albans and had tea at a sweet little tea shop.

Cecil, who has a pituitary tumour, keeps us very amused. He is such a scream, quite dotty but simply gorgeous. The things he comes out with. He has been in hospital for months and will be coming back to Barts with us for deep X-ray therapy. Today he tried to explain away why his bed was wet yet again. 'My bed wet again? I dunno, that dog's been here again. I saw it come in, cock its leg and go out through the window. Look there it is running across the grass!' He is priceless and always laughs with us.

We never seem to get off the ward before 9 to 9.30 p.m.

12 MARCH: Sunday
As I am 'fifth nurse' I had a big spring clean in the sterilising room today and then got on with laying up two craniotomy 'sides'. These sides are very complicated and take a long time to complete. They are made up of all the equipment which is required to look after a patient when they return to the ward after their operation.

Everyone who has had a craniotomy is 'specialled'. This means a nurse is allocated solely to look after them and no one else. All the second and third year nurses and, of course, the trained staff, have to know exactly how to look after these very vulnerable patients. It is a great experience 'specialling cranies' as they require continuous observations and care.

List of items required for a craniotomy 'side'. This complex side provided medical and senior nursing staff with all the equipment they might need to look after a neurosurgical patient post-operatively.

13 MARCH: Monday
Apart from the cleaning and sterilising, the ward work is very heavy – I made countless beds and did five bed baths in succession this evening and many of the patients are incontinent. I can't remember when my feet hurt me as much as they do now. I would just like to unscrew my legs every night.

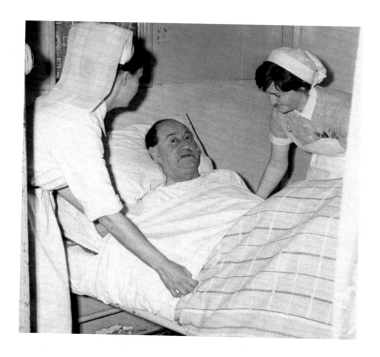

Cecil, a great favourite with all the nurses, was a great character. He was a long-term patient on the neurosurgical ward at Hill End, which accommodated men, women and children in separate sections.

19 MARCH: Sunday
I got back from my day off after lunch hoping to find the ward reasonably quiet. Not a bit of it. Poor Mrs Gooderham who is only 38 had just had a second subarachnoid haemorrhage. She is desperately ill and her prognosis is very bad. We then admitted a man with a cerebral abscess so I had to lay up a full craniotomy side.

We have a very brave woman on the ward, Mrs Robbins, who has Parkinson's disease. Along with several others she had to have all her hair shaved off this evening in readiness for her operation tomorrow. None of the usual tears from her. She managed to make everyone else laugh and even wanted to look at herself in the mirror.

25 MARCH: Saturday
Mrs Gooderham died this morning at 9.35 a.m. When her husband said goodbye to her he was in tears and yet he could still smile at us and was full of gratitude. It was such an effort not to show any emotion.

1 APRIL: Saturday
We are well staffed as the F.C. Eyes Ward staff have joined us. This is because they have stopped admitting patients prior to the move back to Barts – so we were able to go off duty at 8.40 p.m., the earliest since I arrived at Hill End.

3 APRIL: Monday
The Dean of St Albans preached at a special Thanksgiving Service for Barts this evening. All the thanks we received made us feel rather inadequate and uncomfortable but it was very touching.

12 APRIL: Wednesday
Today we received our invitation to Carol's wedding. What excitement but none of us knows what to wear.

14 APRIL: Friday
I woke at 1.30 a.m. to a rustling of chocolate papers in my wastepaper

tin. A mouse! At 2.30 a.m. a cat appeared in my cubicle but it didn't find the mouse. The mouse continued rustling until 3.30 a.m. when the cat reappeared but was once again disappointed. Five o'clock and it tried for the final time and still had no luck. The mouse won hands down but I had a disturbed night.

17 APRIL: Monday

Jo Hamilton Williams is scared. There are only a few of us left in our 'dorm' and last night while I was at home a man peered through the window looking very suspicious. When asked what he wanted he said he didn't want anything and lumbered away. Jo didn't report the incident to the night sister, which she probably should have done, but she wasn't sure whether he was a peeping Tom or one of the psychiatric patients. Whoever it was, she was scared and so is sleeping in, or rather squeezing into, my cubicle with me tonight. It's going to be an extremely tight squash.

18 APRIL: Tuesday

Our last day at Hill End. What an experience it has been and one I would not have missed for the world. We have worked under difficult conditions but that has not compromised our care. It is amazing how few patients have had infections. Could this be because we are in the clean country air or because we never stop cleaning?

Cavell looks so desolate and lonely and so reluctant to let us go but Cecil is safely tucked in and ready to move to Barts, with our little poem of welcome:

> **For Cecil** (in dialect Lancastrian)
> *Tho' life be unromantic*
> *Wiv beds and bottles and bits,*
> *And problems so gigantic*
> *As 'annigan, 'eads and 'ips,*
> *from dear old Cecil,*
> *And while away the time*
> *By lying prostrate on your bed*
> *Admiring 'ill End clime…*
> *But when at Barts you do arrive,*
> *Let Grace remain your name*
> *Or else, perhaps, you won't survive*
> *The routine and mundane.*
> *So let's be mad and have a fling*
> *And 'garter' is the word –*
> *We've tried our best to have a jest,*
> *And wish you all the same.*

NEUROSURGICAL
W. G. Grace Ward

W.G. Grace firm of consultants, sisters and other medical staff. This neurosurgical ward was named after the famous cricketer, who trained as a doctor at Barts.

19 APRIL: Wednesday

Back to smoggy old London (my underwear is going to look grey again) and the new Queen Elizabeth II Wing. The new wing will house the surgical specialities from Hill End – ENT, Ophthalmic, Thoracic and, of course, Neurosurgery.

It was an experience travelling back by ambulance escorting two very sick patients, Mrs Simmons and Mrs Coyne. I travelled with Sister who was clutching a vase of flowers given to her by a well-wisher and which she was planning to put in our new abode to make it look welcoming and homely.

W.G. Grace is VERY impressive. I'm in charge of two sterilising rooms which on first sight look very impractical. We shall see.

20 APRIL: Thursday

The ward is so different from Cavell. There is a lot of walking and we seem to go round and round in a circle, which we probably are doing because if you keep on walking you end up where you started. It's more like a unit than a ward and there are separate four-bedded rooms for men and women as well as a larger, more traditional ward. There is also a nurses' station which is in the corridor and not in the ward, as well as a day room for all the patients.

A welcoming party was held on the ward this evening and was attended by all the big wigs including Matron and the Steward (and us).

25 APRIL: Tuesday
Anne H. and I saw 'Settled out of Court' this evening. 'Free tickets for the nurses' as usual. We really are very fortunate.

28 APRIL: Friday
I bought a new hat – well not really a hat, a bit of nonsense really, it's black net with a rose on top – and also a dress for Carol's wedding.

W.G. Grace is getting back to its old ways – we were 40 minutes late coming off duty.

4 MAY: Thursday
Happy Birthday! It is unbelievable, we have been here two whole years. Incredibly, I still love nursing but I suppose I have been lucky with the wards I have worked on. Also I have been very well and have not had a day off sick. Long may it last.

5 MAY: Friday
Mrs Simmons (the patient I escorted back to Barts from Hill End) died today. It seems even worse when a patient is fit and well when they are admitted and then they die because of the operation – of course I realise she would eventually have died if she had not been operated on but she was very, very apprehensive and felt she would not survive. She was the first patient Sister had known who had asked to keep a lock of her hair when her head was shaved. Her poor family.

6 MAY: Saturday
I had a letter from David P. today, the houseman who invited me out to coffee when I was on Fleet Street, my first ward, asking me out to dinner. I think I will go – dinner sounds good.

12 MAY: Friday
The dinner was excellent. We went to the 'Chinese Bowl' in South Kensington. The best bit though was when we got back – sailing through the gates at 11.45 p.m. without even having to show my late

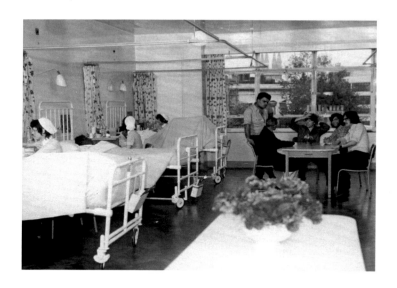

A view of W.G. Grace Ward.
The photograph shows a part of the ward with beds, tables and chairs arranged in the traditional, 'Nightingale' manner. However, most of the ward was arranged on more modern lines, being subdivided into separate bays, each with four to six beds.

pass and then driving round the Square in his green M.G.

13 MAY: Saturday
A beautiful day for Carol's wedding. She looked absolutely gorgeous and we are very envious. What a lark we had all getting dressed up for the event. The patients and nurses in the new Queen Elizabeth Wing, which overlooks the church of St Bartholomew the Great, all leaned out of the windows and cheered.

14 MAY: Sunday
The children on the ward are heartbreaking. We have the sweetest little five-year-old black child called Pauline who arrived today straight from Jamaica with her hair tied in a yellow ribbon. She is paraplegic and probably has a spinal tumour and has hardly said a word so far.

We also have an adorable seven-year-old, called Julia, who has a cerebral tumour. She is a very extroverted, intelligent child who loves everyone in sight.

16 MAY: Tuesday
Miss Dye, the Home Sister, has just come into my room and complained about the noise and sent Anna and Prissy to bed. Sent! I ask you? Here we are, in charge of patients' lives and old enough to be married with children, and she sends us to bed. Goodness me.

17 MAY: Wednesday
Pauline never stops talking. I gave her a bed bath this afternoon and what a time we had – she insisted on treating her own pressure areas.

20 MAY: Saturday
I've left W.G. Grace and I'm heartbroken. The patients were sweet. One dear little man cried when I said goodbye. Sister was very complimentary and some of the women gave me a pair of Aristoc stockings – what luxury!

I am very apprehensive about going on Sandhurst Ward. Sister Sandhurst is a dragon and universally feared. I am petrified and wish tomorrow was over.

GYNAECOLOGICAL
Sandhurst Ward

21 MAY: Sunday
My first day on Sandhurst is over. What a relief. Actually it wasn't too bad, partly because I wasn't there this evening because I helped out on Percival Pott Ward as we were slack and they were busy. It's the tense atmosphere on Sandhurst that is the worst part. When Sister isn't on the ward it is superb.

22 MAY: Monday
So far so good. I was off duty this morning and Sister was off from lunchtime. I wonder if I can keep up this Cat and Mouse game. I did my first douche this evening. Solution everywhere – fortunately the patient thought it was very funny.

23 MAY: Tuesday
Not so milk and honey. We have all been told off for such trivial things. You could cut the atmosphere with a knife. There has to be complete silence once the pre-medications have been given to the patients. Woe betide anyone that speaks.

Prissy and I drowned our sorrows by pilfering her piggy bank and going to see 'My Fair Lady'. We counted out twenty sixpences [50p] to pay for the tickets.

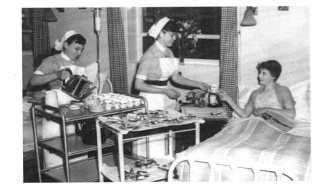

Sandhurst Ward was a supremely well organised ward. The photograph shows two nurses serving afternoon tea to a smiling woman patient.

27 MAY: Saturday
RED LETTER DAY. BETH IS BACK! She looks a picture of health.

Night duty last night (we do internal night duty on Sandhurst). My first night of 12, only 11 to go. The first six nights are as the Junior and the next as the Night Staff (i.e., nurse in charge).

30 MAY: Tuesday
The Queen visited Barts today to open the new wing and Gloucester House, the new Nurses' Home, which cost £386,000 to build. What an occasion. Everywhere looked immaculate and the Square a wonderful sight. I got up at 1.45 p.m. and joined everyone to watch the procession.

The Queen's Visit to Barts in May 1961, when she opened a new wing, containing the new surgical block plus wards which had transferred from Hill End Hospital, St Albans. She also opened Gloucester House, a new nurses' home for senior nurses.
A lucky escape. Just as the Queen's car was arriving at the hospital, a cat ran across the road in front of it.
The Queen's car had big windows, which made it easier for people in the the crowd to catch sight of her.
The royal procession, with the Queen accompanied, among others, by the Duke of Gloucester and Health Minister Enoch Powell.
The Queen meets senior nursing staff, including Miss Turnock, Miss Bartlett and Miss Lawson.

It was a very royal affair.
A cat ran in front of the Queen's car just as it came into the Square. I'm reminded of the rhyme:

> *Pussy-Cat, Pussy-Cat,*
> *Where have you been?*
> *I've been to London*
> *To look at the Queen.*

It only just missed getting run over.

1 JUNE: Thursday
For two years I have said I could NEVER be Night Staff and now I've found I could and I can and it was enjoyable – until I had to give the report to Sister this morning. A very unpleasant experience.

4 JUNE: Sunday
Ray [on Abernethy Ward] has died. I can't believe it. We always felt she would pull through. Everybody at Barts knows about Ray and the news has travelled like wild fire. She was such a legend and it was such a privilege to nurse her. She had been in Barts for nearly two years.
Dear Ray, she was such a wonderful girl and such an inspiration and example to everyone. When you consider all she went through with so little complaint.

A quiet night except for two visitors (Beth and Prissy), who had the cheek to come visiting in mufti – and guess what? Beth has become a bright orange-redhead. Apparently Prissy applied 'Golden Leopard' dye to dramatic and disastrous effect to Beth's hair. The only consolation is that Beth is working on the Eye ward and, as she says, 'At least the patients won't see it!' What will these nurses get up to next?

Giving the report gets worse every day.

8 JUNE: Thursday
A Memorial Service for Ray today at Barts the Less. The church was full of doctors, nurses, physios, etc. and also many medical students. Mr Nash gave the address; he was obviously very upset.

My last night of 12 last night. It's a long haul. After my five nights off I will be returning to day duty before another stint of nights.

13 JUNE: Tuesday
Back on the ward but nothing to do and seven nurses to do it. I cleaned the same cupboards twice today so I could keep out of Sister's way. Several of us often have a quiet chat in the sluice and we can see her when she sails up the ward looking for us so we nip out of the other door and into the other side of the ward and pretend to be tidying beds.

The patients know exactly what we are up to and aid and abet us.

Beth went to a hairdresser today to have her hair dyed back to its normal colour. It cost her £9!

15 JUNE: Thursday

The 'belting' list is up – my goodness this time next year it will be us. One poor girl failed and we noticed that her set had kindly put a bunch of flowers outside her bedroom door.

It's strange, but at Barts you can't be a 'belt' (staff nurse) if you fail your hospital exams, even if you pass your State exams. But if by any chance you fail your State exams but pass your hospital exams then you can be a 'belt'. The thinking behind all this is that the hospital exams are much more difficult than the State and the hospital has its own rules.

20 JUNE: Tuesday

I am at home for a few days on compassionate leave because my father was taken ill a few days ago but is fortunately much better now. I have fallen in love and I think it is the real thing. I know this is a Hospital Journal but this could be life changing.

26 JUNE: Monday

I saw little Julia from W.G. Grace Ward this afternoon. It is so pathetic. She was so fit before her craniotomy and now although she is fine mentally she has deteriorated dreadfully physically. Apparently she has a bulbar paralysis and today all her lunch came back down her nose. She is such a bright little girl and recognised me immediately.

I'm starting another stint of night duty on Sandhurst again tonight. Another 12 nights.

27 JUNE: Wednesday

Managed to get in a couple of hours sleep, then off to Wimbledon and then dinner in Knightsbridge before going on duty at 11.30 p.m.

30 JUNE: Friday

Sleep is beginning to elude me. The weather in London is getting hotter and hotter, the hottest we are told for 14 years. Before going on duty this evening I walked to the Embankment in search of coolness – I didn't find it – and in the end I came back to the peace and quiet of our beautiful Square.

1 JULY: Saturday

We haven't gone into our white belts. They've obviously forgotten to put the list up – what a hospital!

The Square has been the centre of Barts hospital life for well over 200 years and the Fountain, which is the splendid focal point of the Square, was built in 1859.

It was 84 degrees all night. Imagine. Sue Horan and I had a hilarious night, throwing feather pillows and glasses of water out of the window on to unsuspecting courting couples walking through the Square and then ducking down so we couldn't be seen. We had to do something to forget the terrific heat … and Sue, a bishop's daughter. She ought to know better.

3 JULY: Monday
Seven nights down and five more to go. My time on Sandhurst seems endless. When I got back to my room this morning I found a rose in a brandy glass and a lovely vase of flowers. What would we do without our wonderful friends?

5 JULY: Wednesday
When I got up last night there was a note on my door from Anna. 'If you go to my room pronto you will find something to your advantage on my bed.' At last, the elusive white belts. Five Persil-white, starched belts. What a thrill. I have had to make them smaller as the smallest they make are for 25 to 27 inches [63.5 to 68.5 cm] and my waist is 22 inches [56 cm].
    To think, the next belt (all being well) will mean we have passed our finals. Help!

6 JULY: Thursday
To my horror and dismay I have been told I have to stay on Sandhurst until my holiday – can I bear it? Miss Harper, one of the Assistant Matrons, who saw my face when she told me the news, was very sympathetic. Why, oh why is Sister so difficult to get on with? She is so sugary sweet to the patients and so horrid to us.

7 JULY: Friday
You are not going to believe this. I gave the report to Sister this morning and I went through the whole report without her uttering a sound. Was I giving such a good report? Then I saw she was engrossed in filling in the TPR charts.

13 JULY: Thursday
Just back from five nights off. I managed to spend a whole hour on the ward with Sister not saying one word to me – good or bad.

14 JULY: Friday
Meg and I had a most entertaining evening. We went to have coffee on Theatre D and then went to return some equipment to Out Patients

Henry VIII Gateway, the main entrance into the Square and the hospital. Unfortunately for us all, it was locked every night at 10.30, after which we had to negotiate with the porters!

where we were nabbed by a student to help him plaster a man's leg and both arms. Talk about the blind leading the blind. After the plastering we took two plain-clothed detectives to Bowlby Ward as they were investigating how one of the patients had been shot. The shooting had taken place in a pub and apparently all the customers had 'managed' not to see it happen.

15 JULY: Saturday
Had a wonderful evening with my new love. Dinner at Luba's Bistro, on to see 'Ross' at the Haymarket and finally coffee at the Sou-Sol in Wigmore Street. The worst thing was having to say goodbye through the locked Henry VIII gate. I know how a monkey feels now, looking through bars.

18 JULY: Tuesday
I had to 'tidy' with Sister as my partner today – what an ordeal. We have to 'tidy' Sandhurst four times a day so everything always looks absolutely perfect.

20 JULY: Thursday
A dreadful day. Sister was in a foul mood. I can't think why she would want to be so terrible. She must be so miserable. It amazes me that she can be so horrible to us, even to the point of muttering to us under her breath when she takes prayers on the ward. She is so holy one minute and so disagreeable the next.

21 JULY: Friday
Three items of importance today. First, Sister was in a fair mood. Second, I received two patients returning from theatre without too much shouting from Sister. Three, and the most important news of all – I went home for my day off and David Barnes has asked me to marry him and I said 'Yes' without hesitation. It's unofficial, so of course nobody knows and it's agony keeping it to myself but I can't resist writing it in my diary.

24 JULY: Monday
Sister's temper much improved. My goodness that woman makes beds the way they should be made – immaculate.

28 JULY: Friday
I'm on holiday. Sister actually asked how my father was and where was I going on holiday. She stopped short of wishing me a good time, but it was a great improvement.

Out patients

13 AUGUST: Sunday

A wonderful holiday. Meg and I had a marvellous time at St Leonards and then I had a week at home when I passed my driving test – first time too. It's awful being back but 'Guess what?' I have a washbasin and gas fire in my room, what luxury.

I've been on Out Patients, Surgery Ward, for the day where we had two policemen guarding a man who blew open a safe with dynamite, then ran away, jumped into a canal and hurt his back badly. His 'wife' is expecting a baby and is going into the Wigmore Clinic at 47 guineas [£49.35] a week – no wonder he needed to commit a robbery!

14 AUGUST: Monday

I'm on the Skin Department during clinic hours which should be very interesting. The atmosphere seems very relaxed and friendly but I have already seen enough warts to last me a lifetime.

15 AUGUST: Tuesday

All at sea this morning, what with clinics, treatments and teaching, I didn't know which way to turn. Dr Borrie is gorgeous and thanked me for taking his clinic.

25 AUGUST: Friday

We had such a dear little old man with an enormous white moustache in the Skin Department today. He really had dreadfully raw legs and a horrid rash all over him. Trevor Robinson, the Registrar, decided he should be sent to Barnet Green Hospital. I asked him if he minded going and bless his heart he said he was looking forward to it. His wife died two years ago and he missed her so much and was very lonely. If only there was some solution for the loneliness of old people.

2 SEPTEMBER: Saturday

I was in the Accident Box this evening when we had a tragic case. A man aged 65, a widower, was B.I.D. (brought in dead). He and his fiancée, who was about 40, had been going on holiday and he died as he was putting her suitcase on the roof rack. The couple had been engaged for three years and were shortly to be married. They hadn't been able to

"Mix together equal 'parts' of pluck, good health and well balanced sympathy. Stiffen with energy and soften with the milk of human kindness. Use a first class training school as a mixer. Add the sweetness of a smile, a little ginger and a generous amount of tact, humour and unselfishness with plenty of patience. Pour into the world of womanhood, time with enthusiasm, finish with care and garnish with ambition."

Recipe for a good nurse. I liked this item, which I found when browsing through a recent issue of the 'Nursing Mirror', so I copied it into my Hospital Journal.

marry before because she had been looking after her mother and blind brother. The poor, poor woman, she was beside herself with grief. I was with her for an hour and a half before her sister came to take her home.

4 SEPTEMBER: Monday
Why do sons beat up their mothers? We had a woman in today who had a very bruised back and had been kicked out of her own home. Apparently the daughter-in-law was the source of the trouble. However, the old woman was probably as much to blame. She proudly announced that she had managed to pull half her daughter-in-law's hair out. We really do see it all in Out Patients. What a sheltered life I have led.

6 SEPTEMBER: Wednesday
I heard today that Julia has died. After she left Barts [W.G. Grace Ward], she was transferred to Bury St Edmunds but her parents were very unhappy at the way she was being treated and so took her home. She was at home for a week and unconscious for two days before she died. I can't believe that dear little Julia, who was such a live wire is dead. What must it be like for her parents?

12 SEPTEMBER: Tuesday
An old Irish woman turned up tonight. She was not at all sure what was wrong. One minute it was her legs, the next her tummy and then her hip. I gather she is a Barts 'regular'. When I finally got her undressed what did I find? No knickers! Just a vest under her dress and her stockings held up by garters. Although she was filthy herself she insisted on inspecting the couch before she would lie on it. She was a scream.

14 SEPTEMBER: Thursday
At last I have treated somebody with pediculosis (nits!). There are so few nits around these days and it was quite exciting going on a nit hunt. The poor German girl who is on the staff here caught them in Spain. I had to fine comb and then treat with DDT.

16 SEPTEMBER: Saturday
Another sad, sad case. A girl of 25 came into the Accident Box today with slashed wrists. She had tried to kill herself by cutting herself with a razor. Her husband had given her £2 to get out and find a room for herself in which to live. All this happened at about 9 a.m. and although in a dreadful state she managed to ring Mansion House 9000, the Samaritans, which is a new organisation set up by Rev. Chad Varah in St Stephen Walbrook Church in the City. The outcome of the phone call was her arrival at Barts to be sutured.

I had a long talk with the gentleman from the Samaritans who had brought her to the hospital and he asked if I would like to go along with the girl to St Stephen's to have a look round. By this time I had a period of off duty so I went with them. What a wonderful organisation.

19 SEPTEMBER: Tuesday
A dear old man of 86 turned up this evening. Diagnosis: loneliness and hunger. We made him scrambled eggs on toast, gave him jelly and ice cream and 5 shillings [25p], a lift back to his hostel by ambulance and a letter saying someone from the LCC would call tomorrow to see about changing his abode. It seems everyone who works at Barts really cares.

26 SEPTEMBER: Tuesday
What an evening! I was on the Blood Donor Unit and strictly speaking the doctor who carries out the blood taking is not meant to leave the room until the final procedure is complete. Well he did leave before we had finished with the last donor. But it didn't matter because all I had to do was to take out the needle, apply a dressing, give the donor a cup of tea and say 'thank you very much'. Not a problem.

I removed the needle, applied the dressing and asked the woman to press on it firmly. I turned round to pour out her cup of tea when she said, 'It's leaking a bit'. I glanced over my shoulder and saw blood pouring through the dressing and then it spurted EVERYWHERE. Remembering my First Aid I applied firm pressure – no effect. Trying to look nonchalant I sauntered out of the room and then RAN (allowable for Barts nurses in case of haemorrhage) in search of the doctor. On finding him, all he seemed really interested in was whether we had got a full bottle of blood. We arrived back on the 'bloody' scene to find the 'haemorrhage' had ceased. Imagine what a fool I felt – still, better I suppose to look a fool than have a dead body on my hands.

29 SEPTEMBER: Friday
One of our skin patients is a film star. Well, not quite a star yet. His name is Paul and he has quite a large part in 'A Taste of Honey'. It's his first film, and he says it's only a sideline and in everyday life he is a lawyer.

Dr Green, one of the dermatologists, has said he would like to treat me and a friend to see the film and to have a meal and he is going to give me a £1. I don't suppose he will remember, but it was a kind thought.

Prissy has had a letter from one of her ex-patients today – he is at present residing in Pentonville Prison.

30 SEPTEMBER: Friday
My last day on Out Patients. A good, interesting spell.

ORTHOPAEDIC
Henry Ward

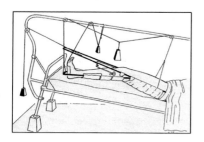

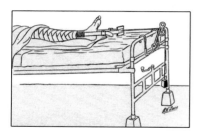

Two methods of traction used on orthopaedic wards. Patients typically stayed on the ward a long time but the young men were often in high spirits despite their discomfort.

1 OCTOBER: Sunday

We certainly have variety at Barts. The two Orthopaedic wards, or rather male and female 'sides', are very different from any of the other wards. Most of the patients are not ill. In fact the 'Motor Bike Boys' who usually have multiple fractures are not only young and fit but they continually flirt with all the nurses. Fortunately, they are strung up in various splints and skeletal traction so we are safe. The work is heavy rather than hard.

3 OCTOBER: Tuesday

Dr Green drove into the Square in an enormous red Bentley just as I was going for my lunch break. He stopped and insisted on giving me the £1 he had promised me on Out Patients. I didn't really like accepting the money but if he can drive a car like that I guess he can afford it.

6 OCTOBER: Friday

I've decided that the consultants I worked with on the Skin Department were all charming.

We have been taught to address the consultants as 'Sir' and it is easy to forget that some of them may actually see a person beyond the nurse's uniform. Dr Borrie came on Henry this morning to see a patient and immediately recognised me and said, 'Hello Nurse. What are you doing here? You should be in my department. Changed from "Outs" to "Ins" have you?'

7 OCTOBER: Saturday

Mary [Gunn] came down to supper this evening with a charming little story which I can't resist relating.

'A little boy was writing about the "facts of life" and asked his mother where his grandmother came from. "Oh, a stork brought her," she replied. He then asked where she came from. "Another stork brought me." Finally, he asked where he came from. "Oh a little stork brought you." The boy said nothing, but wrote in his essay: "There have been no natural births in my family for three generations".'

I've started knitting a pullover for David.

TARVERS ORCHARD, SUTTON UNDER BRAILES, BANBURY, OXFORDSHIRE, OX15 5BH
TEL: 01608 685778 EMAIL: greta.barnes@zen.co.uk

Dear Bernie,

I loved your work - not quite the same at nursing!

I hope you enjoy the book.

With ten miller

Greta.

WITH COMPLIMENTS

13 OCTOBER: Friday

I'm spending every spare moment knitting. Will I ever get it finished for Christmas?

14 OCTOBER: Saturday

There was an easy way to tease a young man on the ward who hadn't managed to have his bowels open for several days. This evening I gave him some Milpar and he asked me when it would work. I replied, 'Five minutes,' and then I said, 'Seriously and joking apart, it would be tomorrow morning'. Well, what do you think? Yes, five minutes later, 'Nurse, bedpan,' and believe it or not he had had his bowels open. How's that for autosuggestion?

20 OCTOBER: Friday

The 'belting' list went up yesterday and one girl failed. Everyone was absolutely shattered. She was a brilliant nurse and everyone expected her to be in the first three. About 20 of her set went to Matron this morning to protest. Apparently Matron was extremely sympathetic and understanding, but said that Vicky had failed her surgery paper and that was that, even though her ward reports had been excellent. I don't know whether Vicky will be able to take her finals again as she is leaving in a fortnight to get married.

I'm in bed with my book of Surgical Nursing in front of me, waiting to be read.

21 OCTOBER: Saturday

My last day on Henry, although I expect I shall come back after Block. I have moved all my belongings to Charterhouse Square. Meg and I have two adjoining rooms. She seems much more settled. Beth, of course, has dropped three sets so isn't with us.

Charterhouse Square Nurses' Home was situated just a few minutes' walk from the hospital through Smithfield Market, London's famous meat market.

Study Block

23 OCTOBER: Monday
First day of Block. It doesn't seem long since we were last here and now – to think – it's our last period of study before our finals.

We saw newly married Helen this evening – she seems to be thriving on married life. After this, we all went to Maybury Mansions to celebrate Angela's 21st.

26 OCTOBER: Thursday
A cautionary tale today from Miss Bailey, the Sister Tutor. She was telling us about a pregnant woman who kept bringing in specimens of urine which contained sugar. Blood sugar tests, etc. were carried out. All negative. She was finally asked if the urine specimen was definitely her own urine. 'Oh, no,' she said. 'It's me husband's, same thing I thought, as it's his baby as well as mine, and it was easier for him to pee in that there jar.'

27 OCTOBER: Friday
Dearie me, Mr Howkins (gynaecologist) gave us a lecture today. He is crude but funny and we laughed in spite of ourselves.

I hear little Nicky (aged five) is back on W.G. Grace and is unconscious and expected to die very soon. His drain is blocked again and I gather J.O.C has decided to leave it this time. When it blocked three weeks ago and he was unconscious, he was taken to Theatre where it was unblocked and he regained consciousness. It seems so inhuman just to let someone die when something can be done. I gather though that the blocking would keep happening and that he would be in hospital for the rest of his life. His poor parents – they have already lost one child 18 months ago in a motoring accident. What is the right thing to do?

30 OCTOBER: Monday
This really is the life you know – sheer luxury, working from 8.30 a.m. to 4.30 p.m. It's so civilised. We feel like normal human beings. 'On the District' tomorrow in the East End so we have to make an early start.

31 OCTOBER: Tuesday
What an experience! I was attached to such a good District Nurse, and what a worker and walker. We walked miles, tenement building after tenement building. There was dingy washing hanging everywhere, dirty children with runny noses, smelly old people, rat and mice droppings – but what a great welcome for the nurse from everyone. It was so different from working in hospital where clean bed linen and nightwear are neatly folded in the linen room ready for use. We had to bed bath the patients and then put them back in their soiled bed clothes and nightwear but in most cases there was no alternative. Dressings and injections were gratefully received and we were offered a cup of tea everywhere we went. I am converted to District Nursing.

1 NOVEMBER: Wednesday
Carol came back to see us today. She now wishes she had finished her training before leaving to get married – apparently all is not well. The rule at Barts is that student nurses cannot remain in training if they marry, and of course all students have to live in the hospital.

John Betjeman, the Poet Laureate, was seen in the Square today talking to Miss Hector. He lives nearby and is often at Barts visiting patients.

2 NOVEMBER: Thursday
I'm beginning to feel ready for ward work again – this sitting down can get too much of a good thing.

I had my reports read today. I had a Very Good ++ from W.G. Grace, Very Good from Out Patients and, YES, a Very Good from Sandhurst. Honestly, these reports are an absolute farce. Everyone gets very good reports unless they are very unlucky.

We had an advanced spelling test today. It was just like being back at school. I got 40 out of 60, which was about average.

6 NOVEMBER: Monday
Sick Rooms today for my regular 'weigh in'. I've lost five and a half pounds and so have to go and see the doctor tomorrow. If he asks me if I know of any reason why I have lost weight, I shall look starry eyed and say I'm in love!

7 NOVEMBER: Tuesday
The doctor didn't seem too worried about my weight loss. I have to come back and

see him in a month. Meanwhile Ormy [Miss Ormeston, the Sickrooms Sister] has sent me off with some chocolate powder to make myself milky drinks.

We old-timers had six of the new set in to coffee this evening – my goodness they seem so young. It only takes two and a half years to become old and haggard.

11 NOVEMBER: Saturday
Abortions and Lobectomies for the test. Oh dear, not good.

13 NOVEMBER: Monday
The General Nursing Council (all three of them) have arrived in force. They are at Barts for a week to see what we do. They attended our debate on Immigration this afternoon.

Still knitting furiously.

14 NOVEMBER: Tuesday
There is a story going around about Sister W.G. Grace, who, it is known, has a shine for Mr Hannigan, the Registrar on the ward. Apparently, Sister W.G. and Mr Hannigan went to have dinner with Mr O'Connell. As was J.O.C.'s normal practice, he pressed the bell by his knee to summon his housekeeper for the second course. There was then a sudden shriek from Sister who had felt the movement next to her. 'Don't worry Sister, it's only me, not Hannigan this time!' Goodness knows where the story came from or even whether it's true.

15 NOVEMBER: Wednesday
A most interesting day spent with the Almoner and the Librarian. The Almoners do a wonderful job and are very well respected in the hospital. We discussed some very interesting cases.

18 NOVEMBER: Saturday
It was lovely to be back. We have all found that we are doing everything by the book. I wonder how long that will last.

Beth has had a premonition that she will marry wide-eyed Willy. I wonder!

20 NOVEMBER: Monday
Another evening with nothing to do – no money and no one else off. Never mind, keep on knitting.

Three large bars of chocolate arrived in the post for me this morning, from 'you know who' to fatten me up.

21 NOVEMBER: Tuesday
We really are not busy on Henry at the moment and Sister sent me to Waring Ward to help out this morning. It was frantic and marvellous.

A Swimming Gala this evening in the new swimming pool in Gloucester House. Sister Lawrence in a bathing costume was a sight to be seen. A group of registrars and housemen turned up in theatre garb and all jumped in the pool. A good time was had by all.

26 NOVEMBER: Sunday
Henry is still slack and as Sister is off for the weekend, the 'belt' gave us all an extra hour off duty.

A 21st birthday photograph, of me wearing my nurse's uniform. I had it taken professionally to give as a present to my parents.

27 NOVEMBER: Monday
There are 21st birthdays in abundance in our set at the moment and we celebrate them every time. It's Frances' turn tonight and we all flocked to her room and swooned over the record of the 'Sound of Music'.

I think I will be last to be 21 as everyone else was 18 and a half or more when they started (which is the normal minimum age for Barts) but I was lucky and just crept in a month under age.

29 NOVEMBER: Wednesday
Photographic session this afternoon. As a surprise present for my parents, I went to have my photograph taken in uniform so they can display it proudly on their piano. But this time – not like in my PTS photo – I made sure I had my cap 'perched' on my head and my hair definitely NOT tucked behind my ears.

30 NOVEMBER: Thursday
Travelled back to London with Bill H. who insisted on buying me a
First Class ticket. I've never travelled first class before and I don't
suppose I will again but it was very plush and enjoyable.

1 DECEMBER: Friday
Beth and I went to have supper at John O's flat. He and his flatmates
are all medical students at St Thomas's. The Chinese flatmate had
bought the supper and had thoughtfully purchased fish and meat
because he did not know our religious beliefs – if only English boys
were so thoughtful.

2 DECEMBER: Saturday
We have the sweetest little girl, aged 15, on the ward. She is from
Ghana and is as black as your hat. Her name is Matilda and she
obviously comes from a very educated family. Very sadly, she has a
sarcoma and so has been transferred to Barts from the Royal Marsden
Hospital to have a disarticulation of the hip. This means that her whole
leg and hind quarter will be amputated.

3 DECEMBER: Sunday
I had to telephone David Attenborough this morning as his aunt is in
here for a bunion operation. He came to visit her this evening and I was
introduced to him and was very taken by him. He has a lovely smile.
One complaint, though, his hair is too long.
   Richard Attenborough and his wife Sheila Sims also visited, and after
I had given Mrs Peaker (the aunt) her medication I overheard her saying
to them, 'That nurse has got a 21 inch waist'.
   Matilda has had such a lot of pain today – it's been dreadful but she is
so brave.

4 DECEMBER: Monday
Thank goodness I am a nurse at Barts. I went to visit one of my parents'
friends who is in the Private Block at UCH [University College
Hospital] today and I feel we are very lucky at Barts not to have any
private patients.
   Matilda had her amputation today and I was allowed to take her down
to the Theatre and to be with her in the anaesthetic room. Although it
was upsetting it was a great privilege.

7 DECEMBER: Thursday
I have been home on my day off and couldn't wait to get back to see
Matilda. Thank goodness she is cheerful and smiling away.

Meg and I got a chance to see inside Matron's flat this evening. Apparently she had lost her keys and had asked Ormy to go to her office to see if she had left them there. Subsequently, Matron found that her black poodle had carried the self same keys on to its lavatory (newspaper) but because she was only wearing her dressing gown and also had her hair in curlers, she felt she couldn't go and look for Ormy. We found Matron stranded at her doorway and offered to go and deliver the good news. The outcome was an invitation into Matron's flat to view the situation of the missing keys. We had a good look at the flat while we were about it – it's not what you would call stylish.

8 DECEMBER: Friday
The Motor Bike Boys are playing up and being very bolshie and complaining, probably because they have been in hospital so long. We decided a hair-washing session would sort them out and it did. We were quite safe because they were so restricted in their movement and we all had a lot of laughs and everyone felt a lot happier. There was a lot of water around – just as well Sister was off duty.

9 DECEMBER: Saturday
Matilda is progressing well. She said to me tonight, 'I'm really lucky you know'. Me: 'Why?' 'Because I've still got one leg left and some people have lost both.'
Knitting. Only the sleeves to do.

12 DECEMBER: Tuesday
Sister was in a foul mood all day.
I washed Matilda's hair this afternoon – what a gorgeous fuzz buzz.

14 DECEMBER: Thursday
I've been 'bumped' 21 times at my pre-birthday party. To think, that in a few hours time I shall be classed as a grown up.

15 DECEMBER: Friday
What a wonderful birthday. I got onto the ward to be greeted with a chorus of 'Happy Birthday to You' and then found presents from the patients and staff on the kitchen table – 'Tweed' talcum powder, perfume and bath salts, a plant and a dog in marzipan!
John O. drove me home in ghastly fog and gave me a bracelet that was beautifully wrapped. Lots of lovely gifts and cards when I arrived home including a gold bracelet from David – not wrapped! Out for a family dinner tonight (including David). Tomorrow there will be further celebrations.

17 DECEMBER: Sunday
Back on the ward but suffering from a severe lack of sleep.

19 DECEMBER: Tuesday
'The Temperance Seven' performed for patients and staff in the Hall at Gloucester House this evening. I gather Barts was contacted by the group offering to put on a free concert. They were very good, and considering they are so famous it was a very generous gesture.

20 DECEMBER: Wednesday
What a day – both happy and so sad. I accompanied Matilda back to the Royal Marsden Hospital in the early evening. On the way, the ambulance suddenly came to a halt in Regent Street, stopping all the traffic. The ambulance men went to the back of the ambulance, opened the door and lifted Matilda's stretcher outside so she could see the beautiful, Christmas lights hanging over the street. Matilda was beside herself with excitement and joy. She kept saying, 'Oh Nurse Tizzy look, it's beautiful, so beautiful'. Motorists could see what was going on and there were calls of 'Merry Christmas!' but not a horn was blown in impatience. The ambulance men repeated the process in Oxford Street and again the traffic waited patiently. I saw London in a new light today and I will never, ever forget the look on Matilda's face – all thanks to those thoughtful men.

I had to leave my Matilda at the Marsden and the poor little soul kept saying, 'I'm missing my Barts nurses already'. I gave her a quick hug and left. Her prognosis is only three months but at least today was special.

21 DECEMBER: Thursday
Home for Christmas – pullover finished (phew) – and then skiing in Austria.

Matilda's treat. A view of the Christmas lights and decorations along Regent Street in 1961. The ambulance men who were taking her to the Royal Marsden Hospital stopped the ambulance and took her out of the vehicle so she could have a good view.

83

MEN'S MEDICAL
Smithfield Ward

24 JANUARY: Wednesday

I arrived back this evening after three weeks' holiday and ten days' flu. I had hoped I was going to complete my training with no sick leave but it obviously wasn't to be. It was a nasty bug, but the good news is that David and I became officially engaged last Sunday. I can't believe it – I'm ENGAGED! Everyone is so pleased for me and very envious. I'm wearing my engagement ring pinned inside the bib of my apron.

I have explained to David that I cannot leave Barts without gaining my hospital badge. This is so important to me even though I can't wait to get married.

25 JANUARY: Thursday

I'm still feeling washed out but I had to be on the ward from 7.30 a.m. until 12.30 mid day and then on again from 7.50 p.m. until 8.10 a.m. for night duty. It was not at all easy to keep awake but now I am 'in charge' there is a greater sense of responsibility. I have to quickly learn all the patients' names and their diagnosis and treatment.

Sister is known to be tricky and very fussy – what's new?

26 JANUARY: Friday

Goodness, three months of this and I shall be a nervous wreck. It is so hard to sleep in the day and I was wide awake between 2 p.m. and 5.15 p.m. and then had a terrible job waking at 6.30 p.m.

We were on duty and admitted four patients, all of whom were very sick and worrying.

29 JANUARY: Monday

My first death on the ward as a Night Staff. Mr Stubbington died at 12.30 a.m. shortly after the Twilight Staff Nurse had gone off duty. The strange thing was that he had a premonition that he was going to die. When I went on duty he was a little better than he had been previously and we had a good chat, but as I was leaving his bed he said to me he wouldn't live to see the morning and he was right.

1 FEBRUARY: Thursday

Jane [Miss Russell] has returned with a vengeance after her nights off.

I gave the Night Report and made the BIG mistake of saying that Mr Evans had been 'no trouble'. She was off and she didn't stop. 'Why did I think patients were admitted to hospital? What did I think I was doing if he was no trouble? Patients are meant to be a trouble or otherwise they wouldn't be in hospital. Had I not learnt anything at all during my time at Barts?'

I looked at her in astonishment and fear because I felt I had weighed up the situation with the patient and he truly had been 'no trouble'.

Night Duty, a wood engraving by Simon Brett, showing a typical view of a Barts nurse writing her report at Sister's desk. The artist is the son of Antony Brett, who was the last Steward of Barts (1947-1977).

2 FEBRUARY: Friday
A late call. Ten hours of wonderful sleep. I feel marvellous.

7 FEBRUARY: Wednesday
I have a problem. David and I have heard we can buy and move into a flat in Stratford-upon-Avon in October. We had thought one wouldn't be available until next Spring and I need to complete my fourth year or I won't get my Barts badge which means so much to me. I'm not sure what to do, because, of course, I also can hardly wait to get married. David is aware of my situation and is very understanding.

I'm finding it difficult to concentrate on the patients.

10 FEBRUARY: Saturday
We have admitted a rather dear old man with atrial fibrillation and pleurisy. He is a cousin of our Deputy Matron, Miss Turnock. Matron rang the ward this evening and told me to make sure we gave him some extra blankets.

11 FEBRUARY: Sunday
Eight nurses have been reported to Matron, including Mary and Anna, because they staged a sit down strike. Apparently Meg was late off duty and just missed the coach as it left for Bryanston Square. She ran behind the coach but the driver refused to stop for her. So, on its arrival at Bryanston, the eight nurses

who were on the coach refused to get off, despite the pleadings of the Warden Miss Lomax, until Meg arrived, which she did eventually in a taxi. The driver of the coach drove straight back to Barts and reported them all to Matron.

I can't wait to hear the result.

12 FEBRUARY: Monday

The 'strikers' were ready for battle. All to no avail. Matron defused the situation by agreeing with everything the protesters said. What a disappointment.

24 FEBRUARY: Saturday

Five duty cases. What a night. One patient died, another had to go to Theatre and another had an attack of hysteria, plus all the other patients. I'm so glad Caroline (the pro.) is so good. All Sister did when she came on duty was to tell me off for putting a patient in bed 25 rather than 26. I ask you. It is soul destroying.

7 MARCH: Tuesday

Mr Pincott who has a very raised blood pressure is getting married again. His first wife died 17 years ago and although he is 65 he has fallen in love again. His future wife is visiting Australia and he writes to her every day.

Dear Mr Duff, aged 79, is going home today – we had our last hug this morning.

8 MARCH: Wednesday

We paid the fee for our finals this morning. Four guineas [£4.20p].

9 MARCH: Thursday

Jane was DREADFUL at Report tonight. She heard a man light a match and I was told off for 20 minutes for allowing him to smoke – the patient is an alcoholic and if he didn't smoke he would probably have DT's. She told me that I had taken it upon myself to let him smoke and that it was for the governors not me to decide if it was acceptable. She was furious.

When the said Jane came back on the ward at 4.45 a.m., she asked me if I had licked my wounds and I replied that I was still licking. She was most amused.

At her final ward visit, at 7.20 a.m., she asked me if I had been good. I replied, 'Yes,' and she told me I was a good girl really and that she had to scratch at us all sometimes. Whether or not she will report me to Sister only time will tell – she certainly said she would when she was hauling me over the coals. In spite of her being so unreasonable, I still worship the ground she walks on. A truly remarkable woman.

23 MARCH: Friday
Sister Smithfield actually smiled this morning when I gave the report and a lovely smile it was too.

Unbeknown to any of us, Anne M. has recently, secretly got married. The 'Powers that Be' have now found out and she has been asked to leave because student nurses at Barts are not allowed to be married. What a shame when we are so nearly qualified.

25 MARCH: Sunday
What a night! Five duty cases, 27 patients, three of them very severely ill, and only two of us to cope from 7.50 p.m. to 8 a.m. One of the duty cases suddenly collapsed when I was alone on the ward. He was half out of bed and then became unconscious and fell on top of me while I was trying to hold him up – so we both ended up on the floor. I had to get a patient to go to the sluice to get the pro. and then the man suddenly vomited a huge amount of blood everywhere. Fortunately, Miss Miles, one of the night sisters, arrived and then the houseman, and we were able to get him back to bed and set up a blood transfusion. As the night sister commented, 'Talk about Emergency Ward 10' [a TV programme].

As if that wasn't enough for one night, Sister Smithfield was not at all pleasant this morning. She said she had had enough of me doing what the doctor ordered – I had given Mr Sims paraldehyde on the houseman's orders – and that I was to do what she said. Honestly, one is between the devil and the deep blue sea. There seems to be very little cooperation between Sister and the houseman – but I suspect that Sister knows best.

28 MARCH: Wednesday
Mr Sims, who was only 36, died at 6.50 a.m. We had been expecting it all night. Miss Russell, considerately, would not allow me to give him the final injection as she felt it was likely to be his last. Sister arrived on the ward at 7.50 a.m. and all she could say was, 'Haven't you made his notes up yet?' I expect she was upset, as we all were, but why can't she be reasonable and act as other human beings do?

We are having a problem with one of our skin patients. He can't sleep because he itches so much and he keeps asking us to make him sandwiches. That's fine but every time we get anywhere near him he has an erection which is very obvious and embarrassing (for us anyway).

Beth is warded again and has had an appendicectomy. Poor thing has ghastly wind.

CHILDREN'S
Kenton Ward

A child oncology patient. Many of the children had cancer, which was heart-breaking for the parents. **Young patients** playing happily.

11 APRIL: Wednesday
I've just got back from four nights off and a week's holiday and I'm now on Kenton Ward which is one of the children's wards. Another ward with a reputation. Never mind, I dare say I can bear anything after Sandhurst and Smithfield and I'm looking forward to nursing babies and children.

12 APRIL: Thursday
We've just started a new shift system. Although night duty will continue as a single long shift, day duty will work with two separate eight hour shifts. The early shift starts at 7.30 a.m. and finishes at 3.30 p.m. and the later one starts at 1 p.m. and finishes (or is meant to) at 9 p.m. It will be interesting to see how it goes.

A very pleasant day on the ward – I'm loving working with the children and babies.

David, bless him, sent me some roses.

18 APRIL: Wednesday
The children are still super and I must admit to enjoying myself despite the forecasts of Sister. I admire her and therefore I don't mind working for her. She is frantically 'toxic' though and bad-tempered but my goodness she certainly knows her stuff. The children are very much her priority.

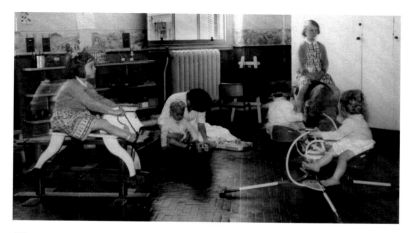

22 APRIL: Sunday
It is heartbreaking to see the very sick children and babies and the anguish on the faces of their parents. Kenton specialises in childhood cancers and for many of the little patients there is little or no hope. Sister encourages us to play with the children and there is much laughter in spite of the sadness.

27 APRIL: Friday
I've fallen in love AGAIN. His name is John but for some reason we call him Horace. He is eight months old and delectable.

30 APRIL: Monday
Little Mark Powney died today. He was only two months old and his death was horrible. The poor little mite died as we and his parents looked on helplessly.

For someone who has no children of her own, Sister Kenton is wonderfully empathetic and I think we realise that it is because she cares so much about the children that we get her sharp tongue.

1 MAY: Tuesday
Wedding news. I have heard that assuming I pass my hospital examinations, I will be able to receive my Barts badge as long as I marry within six weeks of leaving Barts. This is another Barts tradition – marriage is obviously considered to be an acceptable reason for leaving. If one leaves for any other reason than marriage during the fourth year then the badge will not be forthcoming. The badge is sent to the married Barts nurse on the fourth anniversary of the commencement of her training. So, fingers crossed.

Fun in the Square for children from Kenton Ward. They enjoyed dipping their hands in the water around the Fountain and chatting to people in the Square.

2 MAY: Wednesday
An appointment with Matron today to discuss my leaving. Although she was kind and very complimentary, I didn't feel she was too concerned about my imminent departure. It is a common occurrence that nurses at this stage in their lives choose marriage as a priority over a career.

4 MAY: Friday
Three whole years! I think this date will forever be imprinted on my mind whatever I may be doing in the future.

It's a beautiful day today and we took some of the children into the Square to play.

Barts examination papers for our Nursing and Medicine exams. We also had papers on Gynaecology and Surgery. They were dated June 1962, when we received our results, but the exams were actually taken in May. They had the appearance of being simple but were in fact very difficult.

I'm trying to study – our finals are in a fortnight's time.

12 MAY: Saturday

The finals are getting nearer and nearer and I've been put on night duty. Like Sandhurst, Kenton has an internal night duty rota. I got up at 5.15 p.m. and had a bath to endeavour to wake myself up so I could study. It didn't work.

The children, on the whole, have slept well and it has allowed me a bit of time to look at my books but it is hard to concentrate when you are in charge of a ward of sick infants.

21 MAY: Monday

Well, here we are and our hospital finals are 50 minutes away. It's almost as if one was going to the gallows. Three years and what have I learnt? My mind is a blank.

This will be my last entry in my diary until all the written papers are finished. We are not given extra time off and so we will be continuing with ward work as usual.

27 MAY: Sunday

They were absolutely shocking. Honestly, there was no point in working for them. The housemen and sisters all thought they were terrible – so specialised and more for medical students than nurses.

I have been told off today as never before by Sister. I am 'dirty' nurse at the moment as we have a baby called Simon, who has had gastro-enteritis and is being barrier nursed. He and both his parents are blind. The baby has to be fed at EXACT times and Sister wanted to watch me measure the feed, gown up and administer the tube feeding. Problem. She was nowhere in sight when the feed was due. I was left in a quandary – do I make the baby wait past the allotted time or do I continue without Sister? I decided to feed the baby as 'the patient should always come first'. Sister arrived after I had completed the task. I had taken the wrong decision. She was furious.

Marriage should be a doddle after this.

2 JUNE: Saturday

Vivas and practicals today. The vivas were very jolly and chatty. Mr Frazer (gynaecologist), Prof. Taylor (surgeon) and Dr. Black (physician). Fortunately I knew Mr Frazer from my Out Patient days and so we had a social chat for about seven minutes and a three-minute gynae viva. Ideal.

Practicals not so pleasant but passable as we had done most of the procedures on the wards.

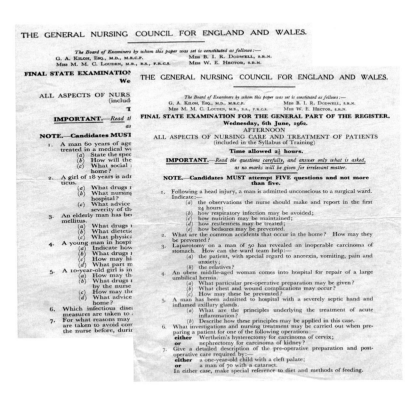

THE GENERAL NURSING COUNCIL FOR ENGLAND AND WALES.

The Board of Examiners by whom this paper was set is constituted as follows:—
G. A. Kiloh, Esq., M.D., M.R.C.P.   Miss B. I. R. Dodwell, S.R.N.
Miss M. M. C. Louden, M.B., B.S., F.R.C.S.   Miss W. E. Hector, S.R.N.

FINAL STATE EXAMINATION
We

ALL ASPECTS OF NURS
(includ

IMPORTANT.—Read th

NOTE.—Candidates MUST

1. A man 60 years of age
   treated in a medical w:
   (a) State the spec
   (b) How will the
   (c) What social :
2. A girl of 18 years is adr
   ticus.
   (a) What drugs r
   (b) What nursing
   hospital?
   (c) What advice
   severity of th
3. An elderly man has be
   mellitus.
   (a) What drugs r
   (b) What dietetic
   (c) What physica
4. A young man in hospi
   (a) Indicate how
   (b) What drugs r
   (c) How may hi
   (d) What part m
5. A 10-year-old girl is in
   (a) How may th
   (b) What drugs r
   by the nurse
   (c) How may th
   (d) What advice
   home?
6. Which infectious dise:
   measures are taken to :
7. For what reasons may
   are taken to avoid cor
   the nurse before, durir

THE GENERAL NURSING COUNCIL FOR ENGLAND AND WALES.

The Board of Examiners by whom this paper was set is constituted as follows:—
G. A. Kiloh, Esq., M.D., M.R.C.P.   Miss B. I. R. Dodwell, S.R.N.
Miss M. M. C. Louden, M.B., B.S., F.R.C.S.   Miss W. E. Hector, S.R.N.

FINAL STATE EXAMINATION FOR THE GENERAL PART OF THE REGISTER.
Wednesday, 6th June, 1962.
AFTERNOON
ALL ASPECTS OF NURSING CARE AND TREATMENT OF PATIENTS
(included in the Syllabus of Training)

Time allowed 2½ hours.

IMPORTANT.—*Read the questions carefully, and answer only what is asked, as no marks will be given for irrelevant matter.*

NOTE.—Candidates MUST attempt FIVE questions and not more than five.

1. Following a head injury, a man is admitted unconscious to a surgical ward. Indicate:—
   (a) the observations the nurse should make and report in the first 24 hours;
   (b) how respiratory infection may be avoided;
   (c) how nutrition may be maintained;
   (d) how restlessness may be treated;
   (e) how bedsores may be prevented.
2. What are the common accidents that occur in the home? How may they be prevented?
3. Laparotomy on a man of 50 has revealed an inoperable carcinoma of stomach. How can the ward team help:—
   (a) the patient, with special regard to anorexia, vomiting, pain and anxiety;
   (b) the relatives?
4. An obese middle-aged woman comes into hospital for repair of a large umbilical hernia.
   (a) What particular pre-operative preparation may be given?
   (b) What chest and wound complications may occur?
   (c) How may these be prevented?
5. A man has been admitted to hospital with a severely septic hand and inflamed axillary glands.
   (a) What are the principles underlying the treatment of acute inflammation?
   (b) Describe how these principles may be applied in this case.
6. What investigations and nursing treatment may be carried out when preparing a patient for one of the following operations:—
   either Wertheim's hysterectomy for carcinoma of cervix;
   or nephrectomy for carcinoma of kidney?
7. Give a detailed description of the pre-operative preparation and post-operative care required by:—
   either a one-year-old child with a cleft palate;
   or a man of 70 with a cataract.
   In either case, make special reference to diet and methods of feeding.

Buckle and belt – the culmination of three years' hard work. We carried our buckled blue belts in our baskets waiting for our results. As soon as the list went up, on went our belts!

Final State exam papers from the General Nursing Council. Passing these papers on All Aspects of Nursing Care and Treatment of Patients was needed to be a State Registered Nurse.

6 JUNE: Wednesday
State Finals. All Aspects of Nursing Care and Treatment of Patients. What a relief to have papers that were not too difficult. We noticed that Miss Hector was on the Board of Examiners, and, of course, she is the author of the definitive nursing textbook which is used nationally.

12 JUNE: Tuesday
I have just heard the very sad news that Lizzy has died. Although we are always told not to get too emotionally involved with our patients, it can't be helped that some are so very special and Lizzy was one of these and one who taught all of us so much. I hope she was well cared for after she left Barts.

20 JUNE: Wednesday
We are all feeling very shocked as one of the twilight nurses, who is in a set above us, was coshed last night on her way back to her flat. She has been admitted to the Royal Free Hospital with a fractured skull and is unconscious. As you may imagine the terrible incident has hit the headlines in all the national newspapers. It makes me understand why we student nurses are obliged to live in the hospital.

We still await the results of our 'belting'. The list should have gone up last week. What will I do if I don't pass? I will be distraught.

21 JUNE: Thursday
I can't believe it. Second Class Honours. I'm in an utter dream. Of the 37 who started in May 1959, only 18 of us have 'belted'. We have all proudly put on our navy blue belts with our very smart, individually chosen, silver buckles. Hurrah.

Goodbye to Barts

A tapestry, depicting the Barts badge and the years of my training, made for me by my mother as a memento of my time at Barts.

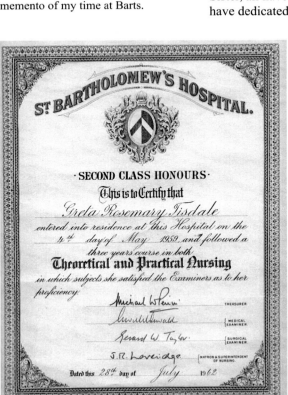

My Barts certificate – at last I had proof that I had trained and qualified as a nurse at St Bartholomew's Hospital. This training set me in good stead for my future nursing career.

27 JULY 1962: Friday

Tomorrow I will be leaving Barts for good. I am going with a heavy heart but also, of course, with much happiness at the thought of my future with David.

I'm leaving my close friends who have made such a difference to my time here. We have all celebrated and commiserated with each other in good times and bad. We plan to be godparents to our future children. What better friendship than this?

As I reflect on my time spent here, I am aware of the influence and example set by the nursing hierarchy at Barts. From Matron to Ward Sister, all have played their part. Many work a 12 or 13 hour day and have dedicated their lives to looking after patients. We have been taught not only the practical and theoretical side of nursing, but above all we have been shown how important it is to put the patient first.

28 JULY 1962: Saturday

The packing is finished. I have said my 'goodbyes' and I have taken a long, last, look at the Square. I received a final, poignant, 'round off' letter from my father this morning. He hopes my experience at Barts has been worthwhile and one I will look back on with pleasure and affection. He understands it is a bitter sweet day for me but knows this indicates a gracious acknowledgment to Barts for allowing me to be part of it and for accepting me within its 'kindly healing walls'. He is right.

My wedding day. Seen here with David and me, from the left, are Prissy, Anne, Anna, Beth, Meg, Mary and Anne Tucker.

22 SEPTEMBER 1962: Saturday
The gorgeous girls, including Anne Tucker, all made the wedding. They arrived last night and presented me with a very saucy, pale blue nightdress which I tried on, just as the vicar arrived, and so had to hide under the piano. What friends! The vicar enjoyed it though.

19 APRIL 1963: Friday
My Barts badge has arrived. With it, is my election to be a member of the League of St Bartholomew's Hospital Nurses. The Annual Subscription is 10 shillings [50p]. I see that if I resign from the League, or do not keep up with my subscriptions, I have to agree to return my badge. I'm going to become a Life Member for £10 – no one is going to take my precious badge away from me now!

LEAGUE OF ST. BARTHOLOMEW'S HOSPITAL NURSES

Hon. Treasurer:	President:	Hon. Gen. Secretary:
Mrs. BURROWS, 3, Meadway, Westcliff-on-Sea, Essex.	Miss J. M. LOVERIDGE, Matron, St. Bartholomew's Hospital. E.C.I.	Mrs. B. E. POTTER, Chestnut Cottage, Greville Place, N.W.6.
Telephone: Leigh-on-Sea 77015		Telephone: MAida Vale 2776

Dear M & Burns

I have pleasure in informing you that the Executive Committee has elected you a member of this League, and I enclose a copy of the Constitution and Bye-Laws.

The Annual Subscription of 10/- is due on 1st November each year and should be paid to the Honorary Treasurer, Mrs. Burrows, at the above address. Alternatively you may become a Life Member on payment of £10-10-0.

If you resign from the League, or do not keep up your subscriptions, you have agreed to return your badge to me.

Received from M & Burns Ap 1963
the sum of Pounds.
Sixt Shillings and Pence.
£ : 16 : -

Yours sincerely,

Hon. Assistant Secretary

Barts League letter. This informed me that I had been elected to be a member of the League of St Bartholomew's Hospital Nurses.
My Barts badge, a symbol of my membership of the League.

REUNION
50 YEARS ON

8 MAY 2009: Friday

It is 50 years since we started our training at Barts and we had our 'golden' reunion today. Eighteen of our original set made the celebration lunch plus three others who had joined us during the period of our training. Sadly, over the years, three of our group have died.

We all recognised each other with comparative ease. Many of us have grey hair and are no longer sylph-like. However, no one was wearing a hat. Oh, how we used to laugh at the behatted old Barts nurses arriving for View Day and League Meetings. I suppose we are seen as the old Barts nurses now. How time flies.

Although many of us had brought our cameras, no photos were taken. Perhaps we all wanted to be remembered as we had been – fresh young girls – as this is how we felt as we enjoyed our reminiscing. Beth, Prissy, Anne, Meg, Anna and Mary were the same as ever. Well, nearly: Beth was slightly incapacitated having only just had her plaster removed from a severely broken ankle and Anne was walking with a stick having recently had a hip replacement. Mary and Anna were as fresh as daises having just flown in from the US with no apparent jet lag. They persuaded the seven of us to stay overnight in a friend's house in London.

This was when we really got down to business and amongst other items of general interest we were able to discuss our shared godchildren. Yes, we had stuck to our promises. It was now that we shared our experiences – our joys and our sorrows – with each other. Much has been achieved by these my closest Barts friends:

Beth married a Barts doctor in 1965. She and her husband Ted spent two years in Uganda working with the Church of Uganda. After this they came back to England and adopted two children. She did 'bits of nursing' while the children were growing up but then changed tack and did a degree in Modern Languages and European Studies followed by an MA. She lectured in history for 10 years and was appointed Head of Student Studies which she did until she retired in 1999. Typically, she couldn't stop studying so did an Open University Spanish course, and is now completing her training as a Lay Reader in the Church of England. Her desire for inventing cabaret acts, which started in our days at PTS, has not diminished; she is the producer for her village pantomime. She has six grandchildren.

Prissy left Barts to complete her midwifery training, after which she spent a short time as a night sister in an Intensive Care Unit. Before marrying Robbie, a doctor, she spent a year at Bible College, after which they both went as missionaries to Nazareth for a short time. After the birth of their first child, they went to Tanzania for four years and then Kenya for twelve years, where they ran bush hospitals and had two more children. They returned to the UK in 1983, where Robbie was a GP until he retired, and have eight grandchildren.

Anne was a 'pink' on Dalziel Ward but left to complete her midwifery training as it was not possible to become a sister at Barts without the midwifery qualification. She did not return to Barts, however, but instead married Richard, a Barts doctor. After having ten children she decided that she either had to resign herself to 'dusting under the beds forever' or to attempt to reactivate her 'few remaining grey cells' by undertaking a degree. The degree won and when her youngest was aged three she embarked on a degree course in Art History. She lectured for a few years and continues to do so if her arm is twisted. To date she has eight grandchildren and is awaiting two more during the summer months.

Meg married James (Jim), a solicitor, who practised in Malmesbury, Wiltshire, which is where she and Jim have lived for the last 46 years. After having three sons, she took a Back to Nursing Course and together with a colleague set up the new, very successful NHS Day Hospital for the community. In 1991, she became Chairman of the Trustees for Dorothy House, the hospice for Bath and Wiltshire. Presently, she is a governor for the Great Western Hospital Foundation Trust. She has five grandchildren including a set of twins.

Anna completed her midwifery training before going overseas with Mary where they worked and travelled together. In 1972, she took a Master's degree in Public Health at the University of Michigan, after which she joined the Family Planning International Assistance in New York City. She married Guillermo in 1977 and became a stepmother of four children. She had a son, Alex, two years later and adopted Memo, an eight-year-old deaf boy. After five years, the family moved to a sheep farm in upstate New York, during which time she attended the State University of New York where she received the Teaching Certificate in Health and Practical Nursing. She became Director of Development and Executive Director of the Mexican Federation of Private Health and Community Development Foundation and, shortly before retiring, received a Masters of Nursing degree. Over the last seven years, she has travelled the world with her husband and has become an enthusiastic bird watcher. She has continued her liking for expensive shoes!

Mary's wonderful laugh has not diminished in sound or merriment. After leaving Barts she took further qualifications in the UK, before going to work at the British American Hospital in Madrid and then going on to a Kibbutz in Israel. This was followed by New York where she undertook a Master's degree at Columbia University, majoring in Population Planning in developing countries. She then went to Bangladesh, Nepal, Sri Lanka and Africa to speak to governments about their health policies and the need for change in women's health care. During this period she ran training programmes in family planning and sex education. Subsequently she became an advanced practice nurse in Women's Health Care, during which time she met her husband, Jay, who was a journalist for the Financial Times. Since 1986, Mary has worked full time as a research nurse for the In-Vitro Fertilization Center in New Jersey and has no plans for retirement. Her daughter, Emma, is working on health care reform on Capitol Hill in Washington DC.

To complete the picture 50 years on, I was able to provide catch-up on **Anne**, my patient from Abernethy Ward whom I have kept in touch with on a regular basis. She married Peter during the 1970s and phoned me one day to say she was going to be a 'nun'. This was a surprise indeed! In fact, it turned out that she had actually said she was going to be a 'mum'. She became the proud mother of Mark. What joy and what an achievement. She remains to this day as plucky as ever and lives a very independent life. She has conquered breast cancer and continues to have a delightful, happy outlook on life despite losing her husband from cancer. The pioneering operation (ileo-cutaneous ureterostomy) that was carried out by Mr Ellison Nash all those years ago continues to be outstandingly successful.

Glossary

Abdomino perineal excision: surgical removal of the anus, rectum and part of the sigmoid colon (intestine).

Accident Box: a specific area where all patients suffering from accidents are first taken.

Almoner: a social worker attached to a hospital seeing to the after-care of patients.

Bulbar paralysis: paralysis of the muscles of the tongue, lips, palate, pharynx (muscular passage behind the nose and mouth) and larynx (voice box).

Caesar or Caesarian section: a surgical procedure in which incisions are made through the mother's abdomen and uterus (womb) to deliver a baby.

Carbolise: to wash with diluted carbolic acid to prevent infection.

Cor pulmonale or pulmonary heart disease: a change in the structure and function of the right ventricle (lower chamber) of the heart as a result of a respiratory disorder.

Craniotomy: an operation to open the head in order to explore the brain.

D. and C.: dilation of the cervix (neck of the womb) and curettage (scraping) of the uterus (womb).

DDT (dichlorodiphenyltrichloroethane): a well known synthetic pesticide, now banned.

'Do a back': a term used for treating a patient's pressure areas so they do not get bed sores.

Douche: introduction of a stream of water into the body.

DT's (delirium tremens): the symptoms associated with alcohol withdrawal.

Duty case: the term used for patients who are admitted to hospital as an emergency.

Firm: a group of doctors and senior nurses who work together on a ward.

Gastrectomy: the surgical removal of all or part of the stomach.

Gastric lavage: a stomach washout.

Houseman: a junior hospital doctor.

Hypoglycaemic: when a patient's blood sugar falls too low.

Ileo-cutaneous ureterostomy: a surgical procedure that uses a section of intestine to create an outlet for urine through the skin of the abdomen.

Infarction: a condition in which tissue dies because the arterial blood supply is blocked.

Laryngoscope: a medical instrument which enables examination of the larynx (voice box).

Laying 'sides': the sterilising and laying up of trolleys with bowls, dishes, instruments, etc.

Lobectomy: a surgical operation where a lobe (major division) of a lung is removed.

Night staff: a senior student nurse who is in charge of a ward at night.

'On the district': in the community.

Orderly: a non medically trained operating theatre technician who is trained to assist in the running of the operating theatre.

Paraplegic: when a person is completely paralysed in the lower half of the body including both legs.

Party dress: an operating theatre frock.

Prognosis: a prediction of the course of a disease.

Quadraplegic: a person with paralysis of all four limbs.

Reduction of a compound tibia: the internal fixation (pinning) of the tibia (shin bone)

Report: a verbal or written report on the condition of the patients.

Sacrum: the large triangular bone at the base of the spine.

Sarcoma: a malignant (cancerous) tumour.

Set: a group of nurses starting their training on the same day.

Sluice: the 'dirty' room for housing and washing bed pans, etc.

Sputum: the medical term for phlegm.

Still: a closed boiler holding sterile water.

Study Block: a period of study in the classroom.

Subdural haematoma: a collection of blood between the skull and the brain.

Sutured: stitched.

Toby: a monometal container on wheels in which dirty swabs are thrown.

Tracheotomy: a surgical procedure on the neck to open a direct airway through an incision in the trachea (windpipe).

Viva: an oral examination.

Warded: to spend time on a ward as a hospital patient.